HEALTHY CHOICES
FUTURE OPTIONS FOR THE NHS

EDITED BY
JAMES MUNRO AND STEVE ILIFFE

LAWRENCE & WISHART
LONDON

Lawrence & Wishart
99a Wallis Road, London E9 5LN

First published 1997
by Lawrence & Wishart

ISBN 0 85315 851 7

British Library Cataloguing
in Publication data
A catalogue record for this book
is available from the British Library

Typesetting Art Services, Norwich
Printed and bound in Great Britain
by Redwood Books Ltd, Trowbridge.

CONTENTS

HEALTH CARE AND THE LIMITS OF THE MARKET

James Munro and Steve Iliffe

What should be done about health care in Britain by what will probably be the last government of this century? How far have the NHS reforms, now five years old, solved the problems of the health service and how far have they created new ones? And what bold policy initiatives - or small, incremental changes - are needed to enable us to enter the year 2000 knowing we have health services which, in the words of the 1946 NHS Act, are still 'designed to secure improvements in the physical and mental health of the people... and the prevention, diagnosis and treatment of illness' (HMSO, 1946).

More than at any time in the past half century, Britain is now at a crossroads in health policy. The most significant issue now confronting politicians - and indeed the public as a whole - is whether the competitive, market-led reforms of 1991 are, ultimately, compatible with the public provision of efficient and equitable health care. The challenge to a future government will be to determine the proper place of competitive market relationships in achieving public policy goals within a state-funded health service. Whatever the official line on the 'success' of the NHS reforms over the past few years, this question is far from having been resolved either in Britain or in other countries which are experimenting with market-driven reforms in health care.

For Labour, the dilemma is particularly stark. It has traditionally harboured a natural antipathy to markets in general and the NHS internal market in particular. Politicians and health policy commentators on the left have been vigorous in both polemical denunciation and detailed critique of the Conservatives' health service reforms since the day *Working for Patients* was published in February 1989. Yet, paradoxically, there are now few on the left who would abandon the purchaser-provider split and force a return to the days of directly managed hospitals and community services. There seems to be a sense that, even if the *status quo* is unsatisfactory, it is better to go forward than back.

Linked to this reluctance to turn back the clock is a recognition that the market has created new opportunities for the political agenda of the left to be pursued in ways which were simply unthinkable during the last Labour government two decades ago. For example, the purchaser-provider split has, directly or indirectly, weakened objections to the introduction of local democracy to the NHS through the merger of health and local authorities, brought into the public domain debates over health care rationing, introduced new levers for controlling the previously 'unaccountable' medical profession, raised the profile of health promotion and public health specialists, given new impetus to the notion of a primary care led service and allowed policymakers to consider population-based preventive programmes in the same terms as highly specialised medical care.

For the right, the policy dilemmas are more often practical than ideological, but nonetheless real for that. For those who would draw back from outright privatisation of health care, the fundamental contradiction of managing a complex provider market within tight public expenditure limits produces a constant stream of policy headaches. There is an irreconcilable tension between the desire to allow competition to determine the nature and distribution of health care provision on the one hand, and the need to maintain tight regulation of the market for political reasons, on the other. Whatever the rhetoric of reform, the result has been a return, as Carol Propper has termed it, to 'planning mode', in which we seem to be paying for the costs of competition yet receiving none of the promised benefits.

In addition, there is now the beginning of a sense of disillusion with market-oriented solutions to health care problems, even among those formerly in the ranks of the pragmatic supporters of reform (Ham, 1996). Such disillusion is fed from two main streams. First, there is a growing suspicion that a managed market may not actually deliver increased efficiency, either in theory or in reality. Certainly, the current regulatory structure of the internal market in the NHS contains few incentives for efficiency (Propper, 1995), and the experience of the first five years of the market in practice provides little evidence that the promises of the reformers have been delivered.

Second, those who expected, naïvely, that market disciplines would be a substitute for clear thinking and hard choices over the future of health care, solving at a single stroke all policy problems and removing the NHS from the political limelight, will inevitably have been disappointed. If anything, far from depoliticising the NHS, the attempt to run health care 'like a business' has raised its political profile yet further. In encouraging us to regard ourselves individually as consumers who should always demand the best of care whatever the cost, and collectively as populations who can expect the health service to solve our public health problems and deliver 'health gain', the reforms have guaranteed a continuing supply of intensely political crises for policymakers to tackle.

BEYOND THE MARKET

A further paradox of the market is that it has thrown some familiar and long-standing issues into sharp focus, yet in itself has provided few new approaches to addressing them. One way to think about these issues is as a series of highly contested boundaries which define the form and scope of health care in general, and a public health service in particular. Such boundaries, which run like a thread through each of the contributions to this book, would include the following among them.

Health and social care

The division between health care and social care has no conceptual basis, resulting only from the historical origins of care in the municipal workhouses and voluntary hospitals. The separation of commissioning from the provision of care, in local authorities as well as health authorities, has emphasised further the arbitrary nature of the distinction between health and social care, since the focus now is on the care needs of the population, rather than the institutional arrangements for providing the service. Yet, just as it looked finally as if the distinction was to be swept away, other developments conspired to push health and social care apart again.

One, as Alan Walker argues in this book, has been the progressive withdrawal of the NHS from long term care, accompanied by a decline in the provision of local authority services. The result has been the residualisation of public provision of social care and a rapid expansion of the private sector, together with an intensification of the long-running conflict over who should pay for care.

As both health and local authorities have attempted to limit the demands on their budgets, the question of what counts as health care and what as social care has become the scene of a bitter border dispute between the parties. But, as Allyson Pollock points out in her chapter, this is not simply a technical issue for policymakers. The health service is redefining the meaning of health care to include acute *cure* but exclude chronic *care*, as a way of shifting costs to local authorities. Of course, because health services are free at the point of use, whereas local authority services may be means-tested or attract a charge, this ultimately becomes a transfer of costs from state to individual. Walker describes the gradual drift of community care policy in the past two decades as being from care *in* the community to care *by* the community. One might well add, following Pollock, that this will also end up being paid for directly *by* the community.

Primary and secondary care

The relationship between primary and secondary care is no less problematic than that between health and social care. The introduction of general practitioner fundholding, the merging of health authorities and family health services authorities, and the development of locality commissioning are among the influences which together have pushed the idea, or at least the soundbite, of the 'primary care led NHS' onto the policy agenda.

At the same time, the once apparently sharp boundary between primary and secondary care has blurred. Recent examples such as the rapid spread of GP minor surgery and day case surgery, consultant outreach clinics and hospital at home schemes illustrate how the 'new flexibility' in the NHS is leading to the dissolution of traditional patterns of work. The sense of fundamental change in familiar institutions is strengthened by the rather premature visions of the 'shrinking general hospital', in the wake of predictions that fewer hospital beds and fewer casualty departments will be needed in the future (Audit Commission, 1992, 1996).

But again, although the internal market has helped to create the sense of change and to focus attention on neglected questions about the relationship between primary and secondary care, it can be no substitute for thoughtful policy development. Nor is political rhetoric any substitute for the facts, as Steve Iliffe points out in chapter four. Hospitals are to melt away - yet at the same time we face a crisis of rising demand for emergency medical care, for which no clear explanation can be found. Primary care is to lead the NHS - but at the same time general practitioner recruitment is falling and the proportion of GPs who work part-time, and want to drop their out-of-hours commitment, is rising. Resources are to be shifted from secondary to primary care - but no mechanism yet exists to allow health authorities to do such a thing. At present the only route for such transfers is through fundholding.

Prevention or cure

How far should the responsibility of a health care service extend towards the prevention of disease, or indeed the promotion of good health? The wording of the act which founded the NHS (reproduced above) suggested that the improvement of the physical and mental health of the people was a central and legitimate goal for the new health service. In the 30 or so years which followed, it was widely assumed that such a purpose could be achieved simply through the provision of accessible and high quality medical care. The loss of faith in this idea coincided with demands that the existing *sickness* service should become a *health* service, making a renewed commitment to public health promotion. The rise of health promotion has followed, both as an activity for the existing clinical professions and as a new profession in its own right, rather paradoxically alongside the rediscovery of the notion of health as an ecological, rather than individual, attribute.

Of course, there are considerable risks attached to looking to the NHS as the primary advocate of population health. The definitions of what is to be prevented and what to be promoted become medicalised, or at least professionalised. Radical and holistic understandings of the environmental and political determinants of health are likely to become marginalised by an emphasis on lifestyle, genetics, and individual exposures to risk. More fundamentally, the responsibility for securing public health is a matter for people and their elected representatives, not simply for professionals. Alison McCallum's call for a minister for public health, in chapter five, is to be supported for this reason if no other. Such a post would underline the responsibility of government for the health of the people, and encourage a broadening of the limited horizons of the Department of Health.

As before, the purchaser-provider split has drawn attention to the importance of local public health strategies, but has failed to provide any straightforward means to pursue them. In casting health authorities as 'champions of the people' with responsibility for improving the health status of a geographically defined population, the reforms have emphasised the need for coherent plans for public health promotion. Unfortunately, the possibilities for effective action by the NHS are limited since responsibility for the key areas of local public policy which would have the greatest impact on health - such as transport, housing, education, town planning - rests with the local authority. To make matters worse, local authorities lack the public health specialists who could provide the leadership and expertise required to reorientate their activity towards health promoting goals. Such specialists remain stuck within health authorities, absorbed in the detail of health service contracting.

Consumer rights and citizen control

Health care serves the interests of both individual and community, and herein lies an unavoidable tension. As individual users - or 'consumers' in the current, highly misleading, terminology - of health care, we expect our relationship with the health services to be characterised by trust, confidentiality, and the willingness to meet our own need for care to whatever extent is necessary to ensure we have the best possible outcome. As a community, we legitimately expect other goals to be pursued with equal vigour, such as an equitable distribution of services, responsiveness to local views on appropriateness, good employment practice, or effective disease prevention and health promotion programmes. And, since we also pay for the service, we would want to see efficiency and the potential to move resources between health care and other public services.

However a public health service is organised, such diverse interests may, and indeed will, come into conflict from time to time. The attempt to balance the interests of citizens and users lies at the heart of many of the most fiercely debated issues in health care policy.

In their contribution to this volume, Hunter and Harrison discuss the different dimensions of accountability to users and citizens which now exist in the NHS. While accountability to the wishes of individuals and the community at large must be balanced, it is only the former that has been significantly strengthened in recent years, and even then in a very one-sided way. The broad idea of the user/citizen has been narrowed to that of the one-dimensional consumer, who may have preferences and even expect certain standards (handed down in the form of the *Patients' Charter*) but can have little or no involvement in the planning or development of the services which he or she will use.

Reviewing the historical arrangements for accountability in the NHS, Harrison and Hunter show that there never was any 'golden age' of accountability in a service which has always been professionally led, either by doctors or managers. It is another of the apparently unintended consequences of the 1991 reforms that, in seeking to bring the 'hidden hand' of the market to bear on the bureaucracy of health care, the hidden hand of the professions has been exposed to the public gaze.

In the attempt to escape politics by taking refuge in economics, the reforms have also embodied in administrative form the conflictual interests of consumer and community. As Munro argues in chapter three, the reforms have ended up creating two distinct market structures, each of which is a response to these distinct sets of interests. Thus it is that we find health authorities purchasing on behalf of the community, while GP fundholders act as agents for the demands of the consumer.

The public/private mix for health

The relationship between the NHS and the private sector provoked little political interest or controversy until the arrival of militant trade unionism in the NHS in the early 1970s. The story of Barbara Castle's attempt to drive private medicine out of NHS hospitals in the mid-1970s, with the resulting rapid growth in the number of private hospitals, is well known. As Rayner describes in chapter one, the 1980s saw a buoyant private sector which continued to grow until the end of the decade when expansion faltered in the midst of recession. Throughout that period, the idea of the state as the natural provider of health care was repeatedly challenged by those on the right, including many in government. Despite this, and the left's almost daily perception of 'crisis' in the NHS, spending on the health service was actually protected, both in real terms and as a proportion of GDP (Office of Health Economics, 1995).

Like other boundaries, that between public and private has become complex and ill-defined in the wake of the reforms. At a stroke, the internal market introduced the language, structures, motivations and relationships of the private sector into the public, which, as Rayner describes, has led some NHS employees to imagine that they are already working for the private sector. Alongside this cultural transformation has come a much expanded role for private capital in the NHS, through the private finance initiative (PFI), together with large increases in the income of NHS trusts from private patients, and even recent proposals that trusts should market their own brands of private health insurance (Brindle, 1996).

In the face of this 'monetarisation' of the NHS, and in the context of the outright privatisation of many other public services, a new debate has now begun on the significance of public ownership in a publicly regulated market. If the purchasers are health authorities, does it matter who owns the providers? What of voluntary sector and charitable services? Where, exactly, should the left draw the boundary of the publicly owned territory which it wants to defend?

Professional autonomy and professional accountability

The sustained sociological critique of the profession of medicine throughout the 1970s strengthened the left's view that the professions, and doctors in particular, were unaccountable elites whose reactionary ideology and overweening power were at the root of all that was wrong with health care. This view was modified by the experience of the 1980s, in which the professions seemed to represent a defence of liberal values, given a government yet more reactionary and overweening than even the medical profession. Indeed, the most effective and vigorous opposition to the 1991 reforms came, not from the public, but from the professions. More recently, in debates over rationing of various services, doctors have come to be cast as the patient's advocate of last resort, always able - and allowed by managers - to justify the desired course of action as a 'clinical decision'.

Nonetheless, there is no doubt that many of the changes in the NHS over the past 15 years have been intended to, and have succeeded in, challenging the autonomy of the professions (Harrison and Pollitt, 1994). But how far should such challenges go, and what are the appropriate limits to professional autonomy?

The sudden appearance on the scene of evidence-based

medicine (EBM), as if from nowhere, is one professional response to this challenge, although as yet an incomplete and contradictory one. EBM seems to represent a renewal of the appeal to science - provided it is good science - as sufficient legitimacy for the claim to professional authority. In this sense, it might be seen as a 'modernist' reaction to the rampant postmodernism of the reforms. In attempting to put clinical science back at the centre of healthcare decisions (and not just clinical decisions), EBM also attempts to put clinicians back at the centre, rather than managers. Yet, because EBM is based not on experience but on new skills which anyone can learn, it allows managers and public health doctors in health authorities new leverage over 'non-evidence-based' clinicians. Further, EBM appeals to politicians of both left and right, since the idea that savings can be made simply by abolishing relatively ineffective treatments seems to offer an escape route from the inevitability of politically unpopular rationing.

THE BOOK

In the chapters that follow, each contributor takes up a particular aspect or theme of British health care policy and subjects it to critical analysis. The intention is to give a reasoned and clearly argued account of where we are and how we came to be here, in order that we can be more certain of the choices which now face the administration. The contributors do not make policy recommendations, and the book is certainly not intended as a manifesto. Indeed, there is no unanimity of view among the contributors as to 'what should happen next', although the editors have tried to synthesize the arguments and outline a range of policy options for the next government. This approach is deliberate, for there is no 'Big Idea' in circulation that can solve the current problems of the NHS. On the contrary, the political agenda set by the right has to be worked through to its end - and we are still relatively close to its beginning.

References

Audit Commission, *Lying in Wait: the use of medical beds in acute hospitals*, HMSO, London 1992.

Audit Commission, *By Accident or Design: Improving A&E services in England and Wales*, HMSO, London 1996.

D. Brindle, 'NHS to sell private care plans', *The Guardian*, 25 March 1996.

C. Ham, 'Contestability: a middle path for health care', *BMJ*, 1996, 312, pp70-71.

S. Harrison and C. Pollitt, *Controlling Health Professionals: the future of work and organisation in the NHS*. Open University Press, Buckingham 1994.

National Health Service Act, HMSO, London 1946.

Office of Health Economics, *Compendium of Health Statistics*, OHE, London 1995.

C. Propper, 'Regulatory Reform of the NHS Internal Market', *Health Economics*, 1995, 4, pp77-83.

The 'New Mandarins' and the Monetarisation of the NHS

Geof Rayner

The British Conservative government's NHS reforms of 1990, constructed around the concept of the internal market, have been presented as a means of modernising its management, clarifying its mission, introducing the efficiency-inducing economic signals of the marketplace, and providing a new framework of incentives as well as better local accountability. These pragmatic and ideology-free measures, they claimed, maintain the founding principles of the NHS and help ensure its survival.

This chapter investigates this assertion in two ways. First, the intellectual and historical origins of the internal market reform ideas are discussed, focusing on the failed proposals of the British anti-NHS right, and the successful development and implementation of the American-sourced concept of the internal market. Second, in two short case studies which focus on relationships with the private sector and on the private finance initiative, the impact of the reforms are briefly assessed. Finally, two rival interpretations of the reforms are presented.

BACKGROUND

> In Britain, where politicians now follow gurus rather than arguments, we are all set to rely on the invisible hand doing a job which, in practice, it will not and cannot do. (Hahn, 1982)

The election of Margaret Thatcher in 1979 and Ronald Reagan soon after, represents a critical point in post-war politics, marking both the end of the post-war consensus and of the expansion of the welfare state. According to the intellectual emissaries of post-collectivism, the corporatist welfare state in Britain (and its regulatory state correlate in the USA) ran up against individualist, anti-bureaucratic popular traditions which had no counterpart elsewhere (Skidelsky, 1995). Obviously it was the Conservatives, not Labour, who spoke to this real public disenchantment. Their electoral strategy in four elections contrasted Labour's Britain under siege (often using the striking image of the Winter of Discontent) with the coherency of Thatcherite remedies. These included privatisation, marketisation, the replacement of collective by individual values, the promotion of meritocratic inequality, and, in the light of both domestic and foreign events, the smack of firm government. According to one view, the USA was, in almost every case, the single source of all these policy ideas (Prowse, 1989).

Anti-collectivist policy-making appeared to be supported by world events. By the end of the 1980s the collapse of the Soviet Union and the emergence of the global economy provided the extra evidence - if any were needed - that the era of Keynesianism and the 'command and control' model of regulation (to borrow Shultze's much-used term) had broken down (Schultze, 1977). The contest between capitalism and socialism was over, Heilbroner announced, and 'capitalism had won' (Heilbroner, 1989).

Yet in many respects, the Conservatives went further than their American heroes (who, unlike the British, expanded state debt in this period). As regards privatisation, to the bewilderment of the Americans, the British appeared quite uninterested in whether or not state industry could generate more money by remaining in the public sector: the key priority was disposal at the highest price. A second area more actively pursued was public sector management. In both Britain and American the policy of 'privatisation by stealth' was generally applied (Pierson, 1995). In Britain those parts of the public sector not immediately destined for full privatisation were subject to efficiency scrutinies, employment reductions and competitive tendering, and, building on this experience, the application of the principles of the New Public Management (NPM). This policy was expressed most succinctly through the Next Steps initiative (Jenkins *et al.*, 1988). The NPM aimed to hold public-sector managers accountable for results through published performance standards and public surveys, to lessen central control over managers, to establish incentives for them to manage resources within overall budgets, and to refocus the public sector around results rather than means. Traditional civil-service based organisations were reestablished as quangos (quasi-autonomous non-government organisations), work traditionally undertaken by civil servants was 'outsourced', and a competitive ethic replaced the traditional notion of public service.

Right-wing policy groups held a vision of Britain governed by a core of fewer than 10,000 civil servants buying public services from outside agencies, private contractors and consortia of public sector managers (Mather, 1991). Even their opponents were tempted by the NPM, with its promise of 'hypermodern government' which was 'lean, effective, highly rational and tightly controlled' using the 'hidden energies' of competition and 'new mindsets' of public and private collaboration (Mulgan, 1995). Some, however, have drawn quite opposite conclusions. It was questioned whether ethical and public service goals could be reduced to the linear concerns of efficiency and market choice (Chapman & O'Toole, 1995), while others saw the trend as an attempt to displace politics into administration (Arnold, 1995).

Although the threat of privatisation and management change have been constant themes in the NHS, the organisation has presented a somewhat special case. Pressed by the right to take radical action, Mrs Thatcher equivocated for most of her period of office. Some measures clearly did constitute a shift towards the NPM perspective. The Griffiths' general management programme and various value for money exercises strengthened management authority (National Audit Office, 1986); the tendering of domestic services helped tame NHS trades unions; cost-cutting, increasing user charges and land sales had cut costs and obligations. But to the right, these actions were at the margins, for the basic collectivist principles of the NHS lay more or less untouched. Collaboration with the private sector remained minimal, despised Labour councillors still occupied health authorities, and clinical decision-making held sway over the 'rational' judgment of management. The NHS remained funded via general taxation and not according to individual contribution. Furthermore, with accountability still focused on Ministers, an underfunded service remained a taunting source of nagging sensitivity.

Only at the beginning of 1988 (on the BBC's *Panorama* programme of 25 January), did Mrs Thatcher, in response to a blizzard of criticism caused by resource constraints, announce a fundamental review. The outcome of this review, which led to the White Paper, *Working for Patients*, and subsequently to the *NHS and Community Care Act* (1990), did not, contrary to hopes on the right, represent a policy framework based on their ideas, but carried forward existing principles reassembled within new management ideas and financial arrangements.

The reformed NHS, based around a concept of the internal market and a division between purchasing and provision, showed distinct signs of American influence. This was what the anti-NHS right, with their connections with and sympathies for, American-style health care arrangements, had long desired (and what various American right wingers had advised. (See Goodman, 1980; Larson, 1980; Lindsay, 1980.) However, there was a vast difference between the recommendations of *Working for Patients* and mainstream American health care. In the early days of the review even the Americanising Secretary of State for Social Services, John Moore, was forced to admit to an audience of hopefuls from the anti-NHS right that America was too expensive and too wasteful a model to follow (Moore, 1988). Those American concepts appropriate for consideration, therefore, were not the traditional ideas of private health insurance and provision, but rather the rising current of new health management ideas devised to bring order to a health care system in increasing disarray. These measures included information technology, new cost accounting techniques, the use of diagnostic groups, management and standard setting, competitive mechanisms for purchasing care, and measures to rationalise clinical assessment and referral. Given the unreadiness of the British public for the remedies of the right, these ideas, suitably adapted, could be the means to transform what all Conservatives saw as the bureaucratic monolith of the NHS into a flexible, dynamic and consumer-oriented public business.

THE ANTI-NHS RIGHT AND THE NHS

The main bulwark against radical change of the NHS is public opinion. Unlike the privatisation of council housing, where the recipients of discounted homes felt like so many lottery winners, the British public have remained wary of the Thatcherite ethic of opportunistic individualism being applied to the NHS. To use Albert Hirschman's concept (Hirschman, 1970), the abiding public relationship to the NHS was based on 'trust'; only a minority could afford, or even wished, to pursue the alternative of 'exit'. Public support for state medicine in Britain has therefore continued to be overwhelming; even a poll commissioned by private insurer BUPA found that 85 per cent of people felt that they had the right to the best possible health care from the state, without the need for private insurance (Pike, 1991), while Labour polls revealed a widespread fear of privatisation (Bevins & Timmins, 1991). Even among Conservative Party members only a bare majority favoured the encouragement of private medicine, while four out of every five members thought that more should be spent on the NHS (Whiteley *et al.*, 1994, p59). Whatever its cause, the British public strongly opposed tampering with the principles of open, largely unpriced access, and interpreted the NHS's problems as primarily those of restricted funding.

These facts were fully understood by Mrs Thatcher, though perhaps less so by her advisors. Hence the numerous health service changes implemented in her first period in office were not to be the root and branch rejigging of the NHS that many within and around the Conservative Party had urged. Her own view, nevertheless, was that private operation and private funding for health care were preferable to a publicly-operated health service.

Over many years conservative policy groups gave serious consideration to alternatives to the NHS. In fact, these think-tanks were not simply out of tune with Labourist social welfare, but also with the Conservative 'One Nation' mainstream. The Institute for Economic Affairs, founded in the late 1950s and inspired by the ideas of Frederick Hayek, had long sought to attach academic and theoretical respectability to its deep hostility to the NHS. Mrs Thatcher's own Centre for Policy Studies, founded in the mid-1970s, and the newer Adam Smith Institute, run by a group of very dry and deeply ambitious young theorists, differed only in their means of approach (and the arrogance of their claims).

Economically speaking, the NHS was seen as an implicitly irrational economic system; it encouraged unchecked collective demand for essentially individual services (private goods), which resulted in supply bottlenecks, and the NHS, without a price mechanism, lacked the 'automatic regulators' to promote technical efficiency. (See for example Lees 1960, Buchanan, 1965; Feldstein, 1967.) By providing services without payment and failing to apply penalties for subjecting oneself to risk, the NHS also generated a moral malaise. 'Going private' was therefore not just a way of escaping the bottlenecks of the NHS but also a moral undertaking, indicating one's responsibility for one's family.

In their early years the IEA pinned its hopes on the growth of private medicine and expanding consumerist sentiment. In this they were later assisted by the Labour Party whose attempted expulsion of private medicine from the NHS (but without granting extra finance to take up the slack or, as in Canada, eliminating private health insurance) stimulated the independence of the private sector at a time when fresh American capital was moving in. Their rising influence with Mrs Thatcher and her lieutenants during her conversion to Hayekian ideas, and Mrs Thatcher's view that the civil service was too wedded to consensus social policy, led to the expectation that the way was open to a health care counter revolution.

In some cases, the transmission of their ideas into policy was rapid (e.g., the loosening of NHS consultants' contracts and the tendering of domestic and ancillary services) but their full prospectus for the NHS gained little more than a toe-hold. There were several reasons. Public outrage over the leaked contents of a civil-servant inspired think-tank report in 1982 kept the danger of over hasty radicalism towards the NHS ever-fresh in Mrs Thatcher's mind. Hence the IEA, ASI, CPS and others were more often used also to test out those ideas which the government would prefer to keep at arm's length. But another factor was that the right's arguments were based on inflated intellectual claims. Even IEA associates, like Patrick Minford, later one of the 'seven wise men' advising Chancellor Kenneth Clarke under John Major, were unable to construct an economically coherent or convincing case for health care privatisation. Minford argued that that replacing the NHS by compulsory private insurance would secure the state both immediate and long term financial benefits, leaving it only to pay for the chronically sick or the elderly (Minford, 1984). However, this proposal was based on costs of existing private insurance schemes, which covered only a limited spectrum of provision. Other groups, like the Adam Smith Institute, built their approach around removing intergenerational redistribution. In their *Health and the Public Sector: A report to the Minister of Health*, they advanced the Hayekian view that health care should focus on younger, economically active members of society, reflecting the NHS priority given to chronic care and the comparative neglect of acute, technological treatment (Adam Smith Institute, 1981). This approach was not only likely to alienate many elderly Party supporters but their accompanying recommendations for partial privatisation - tax rebates for private health insurance, building grants to private hospitals, encouragement of provision by outside contractors, competition among suppliers, and a halt to bed closures - when added together, meant more state spending, not less.

The civil service view was that there was little getting away from the fact that all health services, private or no, were beset by demographic and technology-driven spending pressures. Pointing to the USA, it was shown that despite successful pressure to limit the government's presence in health care, public spending was over 40 per cent of a truly massive total, with the overwhelming proportion of public money directed at the elderly. Insurance-based systems, operating outside of global budgets, were not able to restrain costs as effectively as the NHS. The right's policy preference of insurance in place of tax funding would stimulate more problems than it would solve.

By 1988, damning press coverage of children apparently being denied medical care due to cuts built up insuperable pressure to 'do something'. Gimmicks like the waiting list initiative, which brought in private hospitals to help clear waiting lists, produced only minor results (2,700 extra treatments, and expensive at £25 million (Hansard, 1988). Far more significant were the management reforms of supermarket chief Roy Griffiths, alongside the cash cuts (in particular those required by Chief Secretary to the Treasury John Major). According to Duncan Nichol, later NHS Chief Executive, output per head in the NHS rose by almost 30 per cent between 1982 and 1991, compared with 16.5 per cent for the UK economy as a whole. Since 1982 there has only been a 1 per cent increase in health sector employment, the lowest in the OECD. (Despite the massive management changes in US health care, health care employment represented the fastest growing segment of the US economy (Editorial, 1993a.) There was little magic to these figures. Efficiency gains derived from tumbling lengths of stay and the elimination of long-stay beds. Between April 1990 and March 1994, some 25,992 beds - one in seven of NHS beds - were lost, and 245 hospitals closed. Psychiatric bed numbers were down by 24 per cent, long-stay beds for the elderly by 18 per cent, maternity beds by 12 per cent and acute beds by 6 per cent. It was not perhaps lack of 'efficiency' (albeit measured through these narrow terms) that caused the damaging publicity but rather, as groups as diverse as the Institute of Health Service Management, the House of Commons Social Services Committee and the Royal Colleges pointed out, lack of money.

Mrs Thatcher found this answer unacceptable. Her closest advisors agreed. Oliver Letwin and John Redwood of the Prime

Minister's policy unit (the latter at the time on secondment from Rothschilds) argued that the problem was not money, but lack of market discipline. When new money was available to the NHS it merely prompted the development of new clinical techniques thus generating more demand. Waiting lists were 'caused by the system itself rather than by any lack of funds' (Letwin & Redwood, 1988). Their solution, charging for services, would 'permanently solve' waiting lists because either sufficient money would be raised to pay for services or false demand would be stifled. Similar thoughts, including the establishment of a new national health insurance scheme to replace tax and NHS opt-outs, appeared from other Conservative sources (Brittan, 1988; Conservative Political Centre, 1988).

Mrs Thatcher agreed, quietly, with much of this diagnosis. In Mrs Thatcher's opinion the statist, monolithic NHS lacked the economic signals to create a culture of cost consciousness. Given the opportunity to reinvent the NHS, she would have provided for a larger private sector and supplementary sources of non-tax finance. However, perhaps with public sentiment in mind, she also claimed that she accepted the service's fundamental principles (without saying which ones) and voiced the opinion that the NHS required a different remedy from the public utilities or education:

> I believed that the NHS was a service of which we could genuinely be proud. It delivered a high quality of care - especially when it came to acute illnesses - and at a reasonably modest unit cost, at least compared with some insurance-based systems. Yet there were large and on the face of it unjustifiable differences between performance in one area and another. Consequently, I was much more reluctant to envisage fundamental changes than I was in the nation's schools. Although I wanted to see a flourishing private sector of health alongside the National Health Service, I always regarded the NHS and its basic principles as a fixed point in our policies. And so, whereas I felt under no obligation to defend the performance of our schools when criticism

was made, I peppered my speeches and interviews with the figures for extra doctors, dentists and midwives, patients treated, operations performed and new hospitals built. I felt that on this record we ought to be able to stand our ground' (Thatcher, 1993, p606).

Outright privatisation, this implies, was never to be seriously contemplated. Her advisor, David Willetts, later confirmed that during his entire period at the No.10 Policy Unit, and later at the Centre for Policy Studies, Mrs Thatcher never once suggested that her real object was to 'dismantle' the health service (Willets, 1989b). However, according to Kenneth Clarke, brought in by Thatcher to replace John Moore, Thatcher was 'very keen' on the compulsory insurance model then pursued by his predecessor (Balen, 1994, p166). If insurance remained politically risky, some other alternative was needed which would also introduce the efficiency-inducing qualities of the market, distance the government from the day to day operations of the NHS, and, more positively, apply the Thatcherite ethic of *individual* consumer choice.

In this latter regard, and well before the announcement of her review, a phrase had captured Mrs Thatcher's attention. 'The direction of reform I wanted to see', she later wrote 'was one towards bringing down waiting lists by ensuring that *money moved with the patient*, rather than got lost in the bureaucratic maze of the NHS' (Thatcher, 1993). Regional chairs supported this concept and felt that extra modifications could be made to improve responsiveness to patients without extra legislation. For Thatcher, though, it left 'so many questions still unanswered that I eventually ruled out any substantial new proposals on Health for the (1987) manifesto'. Having got the bit between her teeth she wanted something radical, but without having to stray into the territory of a Royal Commission.

Ever the Americaniser, Mrs Thatcher had her attention drawn to the concept of an 'internal market' devised by US university academic Professor Alain Enthoven. This model of a revamped, marketised NHS had been published in a small booklet and summarised in the *Economist* (Enthoven, 1985b;

Enthoven, 1985a). Given the powerful hold of this concept among the Thatcher review team (although Clarke later claimed to have forgotten Enthoven's name) and its later translation into legislation, some discussion into its origins, and particularly that of its originator, seems warranted.

FROM WARFARE TO WELFARE: ENTER THE NEW MANDARIN

Professor Alain Enthoven first came to public notice as an Assistant Secretary to Robert McNamara, Secretary of Defence in the Kennedy/Johnson administration. Enthoven's key position in the Pentagon, with the responsibility for reviewing the effectiveness of the American military effort, provided ample demonstration to him that the American military were incapable of managing themselves (Enthoven & Smith, 1971). The armed forces possessed no central planning, budgets were separated from management responsibility, and field commanders held too much delegated authority; moreover the military edifice was viewed as politically untouchable. During all this time the Pentagon was fighting a major, though undeclared, war in south-east Asia, and, in his capacity as chief 'systems-analyst', his studies ranged from looking at the impact of mass bombing to assessing the infamous strategic hamlets policy.

Enthoven's unique selling point did not appear until 1980, when he was Professor of Public Management at Stanford University, with his maverick promotion of the Consumer Choice Health Plan to President Carter as one market-based means for establishing national health insurance (Enthoven, 1980). This plan fizzled out, but when reformulated as 'managed competition' in the 1980s was hailed by the health care industry as the best means of maintaining its customary freedoms while instilling the required degree of economic correction. In formulating a concept which was acceptable to both sides of the political mainstream, said the *Washington Post*, Enthoven had 'transformed the health policy debate' (Schrage, 1993).

Neither Consumer Choice nor managed competition was

based on the advocacy of a free market. On the contrary, Enthoven called for a *regulated* market (Enthoven, 1988) which took account of the existing patterns of economic incentives, its structural characteristics as well as the ruling myths of American society - pluralism, freedom, and choice - essential features of any legitimate and successful reform. However, his recommendations are notable too as an exercise in post-collectivist social policy, based on the view that existing state policy had been captured by 'special interests' (corporatism, in British language). Enthoven judged that the credibility of any future arrangements, and even their sustainability, required some degree of social distribution, though full equity in health care, as in other matters, was neither desirable nor efficient.

In Enthoven's view, US health care was beset by two main problems: market failure, which Enthoven thought was not inevitable; and government failure, which was inevitable, and which compounded the problem of the former. Market failure occurred because doctors and hospitals conspired to rig the market in their favour, gaining high rewards for esoteric and expensive clinical measures. Government intervention to correct the resulting problems (in particular the use of cost controls) only made the situation worse. However, consumers too were to blame. Full coverage, employer-paid health insurance, a result of trade union action, insulated them from the true costs of health care and allowed the industry to pass on its inflated costs to the insurers. Some competition did occur but it was non price-based (for example, hospitals competed on the basis of expensive, underused technology).

His central recommendation was the rigorous application of market precepts to root out both market and government failure. This required action on both the demand and the supply side, including the involvement of the government, to enforce the same rules on everyone and subsidise the poor. The taxation system should ensure that subsidies were limited to insurance coverage at or below a minimum standard of provision, and employers were enjoined to collaborate by purchasing health plans (insurance) on behalf of their employees. On the supply side, all legal and economic

protections which bolstered the medical dominance-
maintaining fee-for-service payment model, which fragmented
provision and drove up costs, should be eradicated. The most
powerful supply-side change was the development of prepaid
group practices, more recently known as Health Maintenance
Organisations (HMOs). HMOs combined insurance and
provision, and, by engaging in mutual competition, became
effective mechanisms for controlling health care costs.
Enthoven was not particularly keen on the latest industry
fad, managed care, because he recognised that it too could be
bureaucratic and expensive. The overriding priority was to
ensure that health care operated under incentives which made
the various actors sensitive to economic choice and which
penalised excess.

These proposals were not free of several types of bias.
Enthoven rejected what Americans call the 'single payer
model' as applied in Canada (Enthoven & Kronick, 1989), even
though others found it cheaper to administer and more
popular with (and understandable by) the public (Gabel *et
al.*, 1989; Blendon & Donelan, 1990; Jajich-Toth & Roper,
1990; General Accounting Office, 1994). The reason might
not be so difficult to find. Managed competition had been
formulated in policy salons with the health insurance industry,
large employers and HMOs. Enthoven was himself a paid
consultant to one of the major HMOs (Kaiser) and an investor
in others. The bias was also political (anti 'liberal wing'
Democrat), vehemently anti-trade union and, unsurprisingly
given his earlier vocation, deeply nationalistic. For Enthoven,
other health care models involved foreign - or left-wing -
notions of equity deemed by him to be inapplicable to the
USA. While managed competition 'may mean that some can
choose more expensive health care plans with better care'
(Enthoven, 1994) the poor might benefit indirectly since the
gains of the upper echelons would filter down.

Managed competition generated extra efficiency in the
American health care industry, or at least in parts of it, but
only by rearranging power and disciplining choice. It shifts
power away from the medical profession and towards
insurance companies, and reduces choice for employees by

locking them into HMOs. Terms like 'competition', 'choice' and 'market' have a different gloss from that found in most economists' usage since they also functioned as a device for resolving questions of professional power, consumerism, and social justice. As Reinhardt has observed generally about market concepts in health care, these terms were used 'mainly to further a hidden ideological agenda: the conversion of the health care system into the analogue of the market for food, which offers the poor a bare-bones existence and the well-to-do an infinitely superior existence' (Reinhardt, 1993).

For Bill Clinton, a 'New Democrat' (and progenitor of 'New' Labour) this technocratic and anti-statist perspective was ripe for plunder, although Clinton's use of the language of managed competition in his Health Security Act was not a compliment that Enthoven was eager to accept (Enthoven, 1993a; Chen & Enthoven, 1994; Enthoven & Singer, 1994). It would be wrong to exaggerate Enthoven's influence in bringing down Clinton's health reform. The traditional alliance of health insurers, employers and the doctor's lobby (each involved different reasons), and a Republican Party in Congress which scented things moving their way, were able to mock and undermine a reform which no one could fully understand (in large part because it embraced Enthoven's ideas so wholeheartedly).

What, precisely, was Enthoven's own role and interest in all of this? He emerged, as we have seen, as one of those classical 'end of ideology' intellectuals proposed by social theorists Bell and Lipset. These neo-liberals urged American intellectuals to foresake their role as critics of the new technological welfare state and become its managers (Bell, 1960; Lipset, 1963). Noam Chomsky was one who resisted this invitation. Chomsky pointed to the darker side of this entreaty, the formation of a new class of new mandarins: 'In no small measure the Vietnam war was designed and executed by these new mandarins, and it testifies to the concept of humanity and civilization they are likely to bring to the exercise of power,' (Chomsky, 1969, p25). The members of this technocratic elite, typically people with a professional rather than ideological demeanour, held a shared ideology of technocratic efficiency based upon direct access to power. They established a dangerous linkage between knowledge, technique and power, or 'to be more exact, the *claim* to knowledge and technique'.

In the light of McNamara's own retractions about his role in the Vietnam war, there seems little need to dispute these conclusions or not to extend them to cover to their post-war careers. The World Bank, formally part of the UN, became associated with an American-flavoured policy towards third-world development. (On the Bank's preference for markets and privatisation in health care see Bloom, 1991; Collins & Askin, 1992; Terris, 1992.) In places like the Pentagon, Enthoven, supported by his enormously powerful mentor, could give full sway to his considerable intellectual power. In public policy, Enthoven has clearly enjoyed an even more expanded role, engaged in shifting the levers of a policy science in which he could act as arbiter to the projects of politicians and whole industries. Few other social scientists could boast anything the like.

ENTHOVEN AND THE NHS INTERNAL MARKET

Given the tenor of his beliefs and his *modus operandi*, Enthoven showed remarkable restraint in his advice to the British (although he thought they also needed 'American advice and expertise' (Enthoven, 1991). And unlike Enthoven's complex and ever-changing plans for American health care his recommendations to the British were breathtakingly simple. The central problem was there were 'no serious incentives to guide the NHS in the direction of better quality care and service at reduced cost'. This could be redressed by making NHS providers earn their keep. Each NHS district health authority was to receive income (set according to the RAWP formula). District services were to be run as separate trading units, with services reimbursed according to patient transfers across DHA boundaries. In order for a internal market to operate effectively the NHS needed to be stripped clean of political influence, rates of pay needed to be locally set, consultants and GPs to hold their contracts locally, and despite the use of the term 'internal market', the private sector should also be drawn in.

Some members of the anti-NHS right were already beginning to think along these lines. David Green of the IEA, for example, contrary to the opinion of many on the right, had already attacked the monopolistic position of the British medical profession and brought attention to American marketplace ideas (Green, 1985; 1986). With the announcement of the NHS review, Conservative intellectuals and politicians joined the bandwagon of support for HMOs and internal markets (Butler & Pirie, 1988; Goldsmith & Willets, 1988; Whitney, 1988).

There were several components to these proposals which Enthoven had glossed over and advantages to the existing system which he had either ignored or misunderstood. His model of incentives, for example, was purely economistic in conception. Fellow Americans Aaron and Schwartz, in a visit to Britain around the same time as Enthoven, were unlike him very impressed with the parsimony and caution shown by NHS staff in the use of resources (Aaron & Schwartz, 1984). Not only did Enthoven fail to examine the culture of scepticism found in much of British medicine, he quite failed to understand the demand management function of the British medical profession. A potential problem associated with the internal market, as Salter later saw, was that it weakened the 'concordat' between the medical profession and the state, which had powerfully restricted consumerism (Salter, 1995). Enthoven's one illustration of the usefulness of incentives is in absolute contradiction to his market model. He refers to the success of the US Medicare Prospective Payment System (PPS) using Diagnosis Related Groups (DRG) to contain costs. Undoubtedly, PPS led to a rapid reduction in hospital length of stay during the 1980s. What Enthoven failed to mention is that this was a government scheme, universally viewed as antipathetic to market competition. In effect, Enthoven had stepped outside the principles of his own model to justify his case. While Enthoven is very aware of the impact of high transaction costs of some types of markets, he fails to address this issue in his British proposals.

Enthoven's ideas also caused a stir among health

economists. Views were mixed (See, for example, Harrison *et al.*, 1992; Hunter, 1989; Maynard, 1991; Perkins, 1992; Scleffler, 1992; Flynn & Hurley, 1993). Some voiced scepticism about both the market's ability to deliver cost reductions and whether US ideas were relevant to the UK. (Even Enthoven, on the weight of evidence, was later forced to admit that, in practice, examples of managed competition were failing to drive down costs in the USA (Enthoven, 1993b). But Enthoven had clearly established a new theoretical paradigm - and defence of the status quo was hardly a recipe for professional advancement in Thatcher's Britain. Enthoven's ideas also struck a chord with other concerns. He had vocalised the common perception that in the current system services in greatest demand quickly used up their resources while ineffective services did not. Furthermore, politicians did interfere in management; the medical profession, despite the Griffiths reforms, held exceptional power; and information use in the NHS was patently appalling. Enthoven's internal market, backed by the American health information revolution, was potentially a way of resolving all four problems.

Roy Griffiths, a member of the Thatcher review team, later offered reflections on the review which confirmed Enthoven's influence. According to Griffiths the recommendations which emerged, that health authorities change from managing to determining needs; NHS trusts be established, 'tied into the delivery of major objectives of the Service, not through management line but by contract'; that the management executive and the policy board be firmed up, with stronger attention to the process by ministers; that health authorities be made more 'businesslike'; and lastly, the introduction of GP budgetholding owed much, 'as did the concept of the internal market, to American influence or at least to the views as distinct from the recommendations of Professor Enthoven' (Griffiths, 1991).

Enthoven commented critically on the changes proposed in *Working for Patients* (Enthoven, 1989a). As a believer in pluralism, he naturally disliked their centralism and lack of experimentation. However he applauded NHS trusts as 'a very productive step in the direction of greater decentralisation and greater tolerance of innovation' and he expressed the hope that GP fundholding might develop over time into his cherished HMOs (Enthoven, 1989b). One thing was clear: the theoretical underpinnings of the NHS and Community Care Act (1990) gave to Enthoven a role that he had failed to achieve under four US presidents: national legislation based on his ideas. Though it is ironic that this had occurred on the basis of a 'big government' model of a far more advanced kind than that which he later railed against in his own country.

AN 'IDEOLOGY-FREE' INTERNAL MARKET

Objections to *Working for Patients* were numerous and noisy. Objectors could still be comforted that the cruder ideas of the anti-NHS right (apart from one aspect, the subsidy of health insurance for the elderly) had been squashed. To its supporters the new approach resolved the NHS's perennial internal conflicts and weak management and created a 'new economic constitution in which local districts have much greater freedom to use resources effectively' (Bosanquet, 1986b, p110). American observers sympathetic to the NHS argued that it modernised the NHS and undercut the domination of the medical profession (Light, 1991). Jeremy Hurst, a senior Department of Health economist (and a staunch critic of US health care), claimed that the internal market was merely part of an international trend towards the 'public contract model' and away from the more rigid 'public integrated model'. It differed substantially from US-style managed competition since it occurred within the public sector and was subject to central cost controls. The British reforms thus offered 'prospects for increased consumer choice, producer autonomy and efficiency ... without sacrifices in overall cost control and equity' (OECD, 1992, p114).

Nor was the market really of the aggressive, capitalist kind. According to Roy Griffiths again:

The internal market is not competition red in tooth and claw. The possibility of real competition between

purchasers and providers will in many cases not be
practical, particularly in areas outside the major cities.
The reality is that it is a managerial market as distinct
from a managed market with managers free to place
funds where service can be most effectively and
economically supplied.' (Griffiths, 1991, p17).

This point was illustrated by the fact that prices were not to
be set through the market, but on the basis of negotiated
contracts or actual costings. While the concepts of internal
market and purchaser/provider relationships possessed,
according to Griffiths, 'a strongly commercial ring...' they were
only intended to '... shake up the NHS to new ideas of
competition and choice and to make it clear to hospitals that
they had to compete and be efficient to survive'. If
confirmation of the mildness of the proposals in *Working for
Patients* were needed, the reform objectives were specified as:
better health care, more choice for patients, and the rewards
of success for those working in the NHS (perhaps an allusion
to the new incentives). Later additions to the reform
programme - the Health of the Nation strategy, 'health gain',
the Patient's Charter, 'primary care led NHS' and 'evidence
based medicine' - underscored the pragmatic, ideology-free
direction of this reform.

In the American context, what was most beguiling about
the ideas of Chomsky's 'new mandarins' was that they were
invariably couched in terms of efficiency, pragmatism and
professionalism. Closer inspection showed that they fostered
new relations of power, reproduced old relations of inequality,
and studiously avoided all notions of public participation.
Despite the apparent mildness of the British endeavour, can
a similar division between an anodyne appearance and more
sinister actuality be discerned? Closer examination of
competition with the private sector and of the Private
Finance Initiative help answer this question.

THE PRIVATE SECTOR

Competition with the private sector, said Enthoven, would

spur efficiency. This was a notion difficult to prove in practice, particular given the rather unusual position of senior NHS medical staff and the historical relationship between private and public medicine in Britain. The *Economist* put its finger on the problem:

> What punishment awaits a consultant who is slow in clearing his queue of pain-ridden people waiting many months for surgery? The pleasant punishment that longer queues generate extra private paying patients.
>
> (*Economist*, 1987)

Since around 85 per cent of private medical treatment is provided by people who are otherwise employed by the NHS, private medicine is in part a misnomer (Comptroller and Auditor General, 1990). There is a strong, if not overwhelming association between what medical insurance will pay for and the resource bottlenecks in the NHS. The enduring appeal of private medicine is that of quick access to acute medical services, supplemented by niche markets such as IVF, pregnancy terminations, screening, occupational health, and private psychiatric care. While there has also been an increase in 'complementary medicine' these treatments are not usually covered by private insurance. Private medicine is genuinely a competitor in one sense: the growth of private medicine is an indicator of the degree of public confidence (or at least that of the middle classes) in the concept of *common access* to a public service (though not the *quality* of medicine). Despite the economic recession at the end of the 1980s and its high cost pressures, the private sector continued its upward growth. Just over 6.5 million policies are now held, covering 11 per cent of the population. Private medicine welcomed the NHS reforms since they offered the potential of NHS contracts, but privately they feared competition from the Trusts (Randle, 1990). Private hospitals carry a higher level of more expensive commercial debt than the NHS. They suffer fluctuating occupancy and therefore production inefficiencies, despite more flexible staffing. And they are significantly more expensive. The

National Audit Office's review of the Waiting List Initiative found that the cost of using the private sector was 94 per cent higher per case than the NHS (Comptroller and Auditor General, 1990). Furthermore, the private sector's attempts to restrain costs have been mixed. Some of the BUPA hospitals which offered fixed price deals pitched them above their own consultant reimbursement scales (Monopolies and Mergers Commission, 1989).

The new market freedom gave NHS trusts the incentive to reverse the decline of their paybed fee income. The range of measures at their disposal included 'loyalty clauses' for NHS consultant staff, obligations on consultants to filter their private patients to NHS pay-beds, and the potential for preferred provider arrangements with private health insurers. Famous institutions could also rely on their prestigious brand names (Rayner, 1989). As a consequence, NHS private patient units rose from 25 to 80. Income rose to £141 million (from £67 million in 1987), equal to 13 per cent of the private patients market (Jones, 1993). But the private sector also expanded its NHS work. Total NHS spending in the private sector rose 80.1 per cent from £215.5 million in 1991/92 to £388.2 million in 1993/94 (compared with £30 billion total spend) (Brindle, 1994). In England alone, the total increased from 71.4 per cent to £357.4 million, of which more than £250 million was spent by health authorities, £51 million by trusts, and £30 million by fund-holders.

The internal market, it was claimed, would not only bring competition with the private sector into play, which has clearly occurred, but also introduce greater discipline on professional staffing. In fact, the BMA, as with locally-negotiated pay, has resisted the attempt to introduce convenants within consultants' contracts. Given skill shortages in some medical specialties, management has been in a weak position to enforce them. Likewise the introduction of job plans and the monitoring of consultant workloads remains more theoretical than real. The increase in private work, on the other hand, has meant that many consultants have other fish to fry: one hour of consultant's time in the private sector is worth up to six times their NHS income. Consequently, public patients have suffered. One study reported that one-third of consultants missed more than one in ten clinics and 10 per cent of consultants recorded difficulties in juggling private and NHS commitments, while the remainder made 'other arrangements'. These 'other arrangements' meant that junior doctors were left to operate; often 'beyond their competence' (Audit Commission, 1995a).

Non-fundholding GPs have no incentive to refer their patients to the private sector as they receive no fee for making the referral. GP fundholders, however, can purchase care on their own account. And if the patient is medically insured, the fund-holder has a financial incentive to refer privately (much to the chagrin of the insurance companies). NHS hospital trusts now have the incentive to ask patients if they are privately insured.

THE PRIVATE FINANCE INITIATIVE

Alongside the streaming of private and public patients, of potentially greatest impact on the 'public' future of the NHS is the private finance initiative. This was not, as noted, part of the original reform package. When the use of private finance was first mooted in the NHS review it caused alarm within the Treasury, which feared that schemes could not be monitored and might run out of control (Hencke, 1988).

The proposals continued to be promoted by Mrs Thatcher's advisors. To David Willetts, support for PFI was a matter of 'managerial and political will. If it is clear that Ministers and the Management Executive support such development then there is undoubtedly enormous scope for schemes ... If Ministers and the Management Executive seek to defend publicly owned and managed provision at all costs, then these schemes will stay in the limbo where they have languished for the past decade' (Willets, 1993). Over time, ministers, motivated first by the need to reduce public sector borrowing, and then sensing that Labour risked charges of hypocrisy by opposing PFI, soon gave the go-ahead. New NHS guidance was released (NHS Management Executive, 1993).

PFI is a long-winded process, fraught with difficulty. Nevertheless it was increasingly becoming a 'best option' since existing sources of capital funding were running dry. One survey showed that one-third expected to use sales as their main source of funds; almost one-quarter expected to use finance from banks, leasing arrangements or some other private-sector source to support investments (Taylor, 1994). The property slump reduced income from capital schemes, and the resulting decline in NHS capital projects drew protests from the building industry (Blair, 1995).

In the 1995 Budget, a score of PFI schemes were announced, some involving entire hospitals built and operated by the private sector. The fact that Stephen Dorrell, the new Secretary of State for Health, saw that the PFI laid him open to charges of privatisation, is indicated by the wording of the Department's press release: 'Patients before politics: PFI reinforces founding principle of the NHS'. Dorrell's accompanying statement noted:

> The Trust itself will continue to be the direct employer of clinical staff. It is no part of the Government's policy to transfer the delivery of NHS clinical services into the private sector. The PFI is about the provision of the supporting facilities. It sets out to ensure that they are as modern and efficient as we can make them by subcontracting responsibility for their provision to specialist managers who are expert at providing them (Department of Health, 1995).

A new definition of the NHS had been established. No longer was it defined comprehensively but merely according to its core clinical dimensions; everything else was potentially operated by private sector 'experts'.

But, as with the internal market, private finance poses dilemmas for the longer term. Trusts will not be able to renege on repayment of their capital interest (as we saw earlier), and the cost of the capital will be higher. Such a move in the longer term will place the NHS in a position of parity with the private sector.

CONCLUSION: 'MONETARISING' THE NHS?

Two quite different views of the NHS reforms might be defined. The first focuses on the unprecedented expectations placed on the Smithian 'hidden hand' of the market (see Hahn's remark at the beginning of this chapter) and its stuttering and confused beginnings. Enthoven suggested, and Griffiths confirmed, that the principles guiding the establishment of an internal market in the NHS were more closely akin to market socialism than capitalism. But perhaps, in the process, a deformed Soviet-style system was also set in place. A system operated by a nomenklatura of political appointees, guided a management which used technocratic language to mask political choices and which used bureaucratic fixes to overcome its operating systems' intrinsic theoretical and practical flaws. And as in Soviet Russia, there has been a creeping accommodation with capitalism. Even those apparently positive aspects of the reforms not considered here - the Health of the Nation, health gain, primary care-led health care, evidence-based medicine, etc - might be viewed merely as distractions or triumphant anouncements to keep the wobbling enterprise upright.

A second, rival view would emphasise the success of the NHS's managerial and technical modernisation: the shift towards out-patient treatment, rising productivity, the movement from an 'undermanaged' to a 'managed' service, new codes of practice for accountability and openness, better guidance on complaints, more open consumer choice and treatment guarantees; all of this accompanied by the gradual softening of market rhetoric. Waiting lists, like examination results, were the proof that the lessons of good management had been learnt; a rejuvenated NHS had shifted from a sickness service to a wellness service. Mrs Bottomley, just before handing over to Stephen Dorrell, confirmed in almost socialist tones, the spirit of these changes:

> The NHS is not a business. The only profit it makes is measured in the cure of illness, the care of the sick, the relief of pain and its contribution to a healthier nation.

> We are all its shareholders; but our interest is human, not financial (Bottomley, 1995).

In the light of some of the evidence discussed, which view better fits the facts? Our purpose was to assess the degree to which the NHS reforms, in the name of a pragmatic approach to modernisation, had managed to avoid the recommendations of the anti-NHS right. While Enthoven's recommendations for an internal market differed substantially from those of managed competition in the USA, a number of important philosophical elements were carried over, including the need to nullify the essential political nature of choice through technocratic means.

But given that historical institutions like the NHS carry a momentum of their own, it could never be expected that a new discourse could simply displace an existing one. The reforms are merely an additional model of social relations transposed over an existing format of professional and patient relations and expectations. Of course, over time economic forces glacially remake the underlying bedrock of practices, behaviours and ethics. The *Financial Times*, attempting to gauge the long-term impact of the reforms, has expressed similar thoughts. It observed that the NHS's administrative costs were previously low because the service had avoided elaborate pricing and invoicing mechanisms. Because the forces of the new, invoice-driven market had their own way of imposing their priorities on their participants it would create 'irresistible pressures - on the part of both hospitals and GPs - for partial or complete privatisation of health care' (Editorial, 1989).

There are signs that the cultural effects are becoming embedded in the new management relations. One example is the apparent acceptability of both deception and cynicism in the development of a competitive strategy for trusts. The advice offered to NHS managers by Coad and Kennedy of the Institute of Health Service Management is one telling example. Survival in the new NHS market, they state, requires managers to gather intelligence on their competitors, rigorously assess the marketplace to define the best fit between product and demand, and realistically assess their customers:

> ...there is clearly no point in offering five-star-hotel services if the unit is providing services within a depressed area with a high unemployment rate and a sociological profile which would not be able to take advantage of such services (Coad & Kennedy, 1992).

The poor, as we remember Enthoven advised in his managed competition scheme, must for reasons of practicality and efficiency, be denied the economic choices of those above them.

In the NHS, the focus on incentives, the encouragement of economic competition between trusts, the splintering of purchasing decisions into individual items of service, and the use of care management to undertake financial assessment all indicate moves in this direction. If the mechanisms for discrimination between patients are already in place, the remaining issue is the speed by which they begin to operate. In the USA the discrimination between the insured and non-insured first began by charitable institutions asking to see their patient's insurance details; it ended with the exclusion (more usually transfer) of patients without them. A hospital system initially constructed around a charitable ethic, became, over time, merely a normal business enterprise (Rosenberg 1987; Stevens, 1989). There is also a term to describe this process. Veteran American health economist Eli Ginzberg has coined the term 'monetarisation' to describe the conversion of health care to the values of success based on money alone (Ginzberg, 1984).

Privatisation, long desired by the anti-NHS right, should not be seen in terms of a single point of outcome, but as stages along a continuum. Duncan Nichol, like Enthoven a candidate for mandarinhood, has since leaving the NHS become associated with the asking of 'tough questions' that push services in this direction. For example: What core services should the NHS provide free at the point of use? 'What about other sources of funding such as co-payment?' (Nichol, Sir D.,

1996). Of course, the success of privatisation as an objective in structural terms is inevitably linked to the political success of its advocates. In this regard, concluding this chapter with the thoughts of John Redwood, a potential leader of the Conservative Party, might be apt:

> But need there be just one leap? Might it not, rather, be possible to work slowly from the present system towards a national insurance scheme? One could begin, for example, with the establishment of the NHS as an independent trust, with increased joint ventures between the NHS and the private sector; move on next to the use of 'credits' to meet standard charges set by a central NHS funding administration for independently managed hospitals or districts; and only at the last stage create a national health insurance scheme separate from the tax system (Letwin & Redwood, 1988, p19).

References

H. J. Aaron and W. B. Schwartz, *The Painful Prescription: rationing hospital care*, Brookings Institute, Washington DC 1984.

Adam Smith Institute, *Health and the Public Sector: A Report to the Minister of Health*, Adam Smith Institute, London 1981.

J. E. Alt, *The Politics of Economic Decline*, Cambridge University Press, Cambridge 1979.

Anon., 'NHS Trusts Chiefs Average 8.9% Rise', *Financial Times*, 29 November 1993.

P.E. Arnold, 'Reform's Changing Role' *Public Administration Review*, 55(5), 1995, pp407-417.

Audit Commission, *The Doctors' Tale: the work of hospital doctors in England and Wales*, The Audit Commission, London 1995a.

The Audit Commission, *A Price on Their Heads: measuring management costs in NHS Trusts*, HMSO, London 1995b.

M. Balen, *Kenneth Clarke*, Fourth Estate, London 1994.

D. Bell, *The End of Ideology: on the exhaustion of political ideas in the fifties*, Free Press of Glencoe, Glencoe, Illinois 1960.

A. Bevins and N. Timmins, 'NHS Fears Identified As Tories' Biggest Obstacle', *The Independent*, 18 September 1991, p1.

L Blair, 'Cutbacks Brings Hospital Repairs to Grinding Halt', *Evening Standard*, 21 April 1995, p2.

R. J. Blendon and K. Donelan, 'The Public and the Emerging Debate Over National Health Insurance', *New England Journal of Medicine*, 323(3), 19 July 1990, pp208-212.

G. Bloom, *States of Markets: neo-liberalism and the development policy debate. Managing health sector developments: markets and institutional reform*, Clarendon Press, Oxford 1991.

N. Bosanquet, (ed), 'Health Care UK 1986. GPs As Firms: Creating an internal market for primary care', *Policy Journals*, pp65-68, Hermitage, Berks 1986a.

N. Bosanquet, 'Inconsistencies of the NHS: Buchanan Revisited', Pp. in *Public and Private Health Services*. Basil Blackwell, Oxford 1986b.

V. Bottomley, *The New NHS: Continuity and Change*, Department of Health (Press Release), London, 20 June 1995.

D. Brindle, 'NHS Private Care Up 80pc', *The Guardian*, 28 December 1994, p7.

L. Brittan, *A new deal for health care*, Conservative Political Centre, London 1988.

J. Buchan, 'The Hidden Agenda', *Nursing Times*, 85(8), 22 February 1989, p20.

J. Buchanan, *The Inconsistencies of the NHS*, Institute of Economic Affairs, London 1965.

E. Butler, (ed), *Unhealthy Competition*, Adam Smith Institute, London 1994.

E. Butler and M. Pirie, *The Health of Nations*. Adam Smith Institute, London 1988.

E. Caines, 'A Case of Old Wine in New Bottles', *Parliamentary Brief*, November 1995, pp48-50.

R. A. Chapman and B. J. O'Toole, 'The Role of the Civil Service: A Traditional View in a Period of Change', *Public Policy and Administration*, 10(2), pp3-20, 1995.

E. Chen and A. C. Enthoven, 'Key Economist Flays Clinton Health Plan', *Los Angeles Times,* 13 January 1994, p8.

N. Chomsky, *American Power and the New Mandarins*, Penguin Books, Harmondsworth 1969.

H. Coad and B. Kennedy, 'Competitive Strategies in the NHS', *Health Services Management*, 88, 2 April 1992, pp11,13.

R. Cockett, *Thinking the Unthinkable: think tanks and the economic counter-revolution*, HarperCollins, London 1995.

C. Collins and S. Askin, 'World Bank and Heritage Dump On Third World', *National Catholic Reporter*, 28 February 1992, p8.

Comptroller and Auditor General, *The NHS and Independent Hospitals*, HMSO/National Audit Office, London, December 1990.

Conservative Political Centre, *A New Deal for Health Care*, Conservative Party, London 1988.

D. Dawson, *Costs and Prices in the Internal Market*, Do LE-Cambridge University, Cambridge, July 1994.

Department of Health, *Patients before Politics: PFI reinforces founding principle of the NHS*, Press Release, Department of Health, London, 21 November 1995.

Department of Health, *Government Response to the First Report from the Health Committee, Session 1992-93, NHS Trusts: Interim conclusions and proposals for future inquiries*, DoH, Cm 2152, London, February 1993.

R. Dyson, *Changing Labour Utilisation and NHS Trusts*, NHS Management Executive, London 1992.

Economist, 'Underclass Issues', *The Economist*, 23 May 1987, pp13-14.

Economist, 'Britain's Sickly Health Reforms', *The Economist*, 19 February 1994, pp16-17.

Economist, 'John Major V the Nurses', *The Economist*, 15 April 1995a, p18.

Economist, 'Stealth School, You Might Say', 29 July 1995b, p43.

Editorial, 'Mr Clarke's Health Reforms', *Financial Times*, 21 February 1989, p20.

Editorial, 'Jobs,Jobs,Jobs', Business Week, 22 February 1993a, pp68-74.

Editorial, 'Opening Up On Health Care', *New York Times*, 7 March 1993b, p16.

Editorial, 'Redwood Sees the Light', *Evening Standard*, 17 November 1993c, p9.

P. M. Ellwood, N. N. Anderson, J. E. Billings, R. J. Carlson, E. J. Hoagberg, and W. McClure, 'The Health Maintenance Strategy', *Medical Care*, 9 June 1971, pp291-298.

A.C. Enthoven, *Health Plan: the only practical solution to the soaring cost of medical care*, Addison Wesley Publishing Co., Reading, Mass., 1980.

A.C. Enthoven, 'National Health Service: Some Reforms That Might Be Politically Feasible', *The Economist*, 22 June 1985a, pp19-22.

A.C. Enthoven, *Reflections on the management of the National Health Service*, Nuffield Provincial Hospitals Trust, London 1985b.

A.C. Enthoven, 'Managed Competition of Alternative Delivery Systems', *J Health Polit Policy Law*, 13(2) Summer 1988, pp305-321.

A.C. Enthoven, 'NHS Review. Words from the Source: An Interview With Alain Enthoven [Interview By R.Smith]', *British Medical Journal*, 298 (6681), 29 April 1989a, pp1166-1168.

A.C. Enthoven, 'What Can Europeans Learn from Americans?' *Health Care Financing Review*, Annual supplement 1989b, pp49-63.

A.C. Enthoven, 'Internal Reform of the British National Health Service', *Health Affairs (Millwood)*, 10(3) 1991, pp60-70.

A. C. Enthoven, 'A Good Health Care Idea Gone Bad' *The Wall Street Journal*, 7 October 1993a, p18.

A. C. Enthoven, 'Why Managed Care Has Failed to Contain Costs', *Health Affairs (Millwood)*, 12(3), Fall 1993b, pp27-43.

A. C. Enthoven, 'On the Ideal Market Structure for Third-Party Purchasing of Health Care', *Social Science and Medicine*, 39(10), November 1994, pp1413-1424.

A. C. Enthoven and R. Kronick, 'A Consumer-Choice Health Plan for the 1990s. Universal Health Insurance in a System Designed to Promote Quality and Economy (2)', *New England Journal of Medicine*, 320(2), 12 Jan 1989, pp94-101.

A. C. Enthoven and S. J. Singer, 'A Single-Payer System in Jackson Hole Clothing', *Health Affairs (Millwood)*, 13(1), Spring 1994, pp81-95.

A. C. Enthoven and K. W. Smith, *How Much is Enough? Shaping the defense program*, Harper and Row, New York 1971.

M. S. Feldstein, *Economic Analysis for Health Service Efficiency*, North Holland Publishing Company, Amsterdam 1967.

B. Ferguson and J. Posnett, 'Pricing in the NHS Internal Market', *Health Economics*, 3, 1994, pp133-136.

N. Flynn and D. Hurley, *The Market for Care*, London School of Economics and Political Science, Public Sector Management,

London 1993.

J. H. Gabel, H. Cohen and S. Fink, 'Americans' Views On Health Care: Foolish Inconsistencies?' *Health Affairs (Millwood)*, 8(1), Spring 1989, pp103-118.

E. Ginzberg, 'The Monetarization of Medical Care', *New England Journal of Medicine*, 310(18), 3 May 1984, pp1162-1165.

M. Goldsmith and D. Willets, *Managed Healthcare*, Centre for Policy Studies, London 1988.

J. C. Goodman, *National Health Care in Great Britain: lessons for the U.S.A.*, Fisher Institute, Dallas, Texas 1980.

A. Gore, *From Red Tape to Results: creating a national government that works better*, Report of the National Performance Review, Vice President Al Gore, September 7 1993.

D. G. Green, *Which Doctor?: a critical analysis of the professional barriers to competition in health care*, Institute of Economic Affairs, London 1985.

D. G. Green, *Challenge to the NHS: a study of competition in America's health care and the lessons for Britain*, IEA, London 1986.

Sir Roy Griffiths, *7 years of progress - general management in the NHS*, No.3, 12 June 1991, The Audit Commission for Local Authorities and the National Health Service in England and Wales, London.

F. Hahn, 'Reflections On the Invisible Hand', *Lloyds Bank Review*, 144, April 1982, pp1-21.

Hansard, Private hospitals (unused capacity), No. 1433, 11 January 1988, Written Answers, col.239.

S. Harrison, D. J. Hunter, I. Johnston and G. Wistow, *Competing for Health: a commentary on the NHS review*, Leeds University, Nuffield Institute for Health Services Studies, Leeds 1992.

R. Heilbroner, 'The Triumph of Capitalism', *New York Magazine*, 23 January 1989, pp98-109.

D. Hencke, 'Hospital Leasing Plan Irks Treasury', *The Guardian*, 6 October 1988, p1.

A. O. Hirschman, *Exit, Voice and Loyalty*, Harvard University Press, Cambridge, Mass., 1970.

HM Treasury, *Using Private Enterprise in Government. Report of a multi-departmental review of competitive tendering and contracting for services in Government Departments*, HMSO, London 1986.

C. Holland, 'Single Specialty Trusts Fall into the "Management Gap"', *British Journal of Health Care Management*, 1(1), pp8-9.

P. Hunt, 'Accountability in the National Health Service', *Parliamentary Affairs*, 1995, pp297-305.

D. Hunter, 'First Define Your Terms', *Health Service Journal*, 30 November 1989, p1475.

C. Jajich-Toth and B. W. Roper, 'Views On Health Care: A Study in Contradictions', *Health Affairs (Millwood)*, 9(4), Winter 1990, pp149-157.

K. Jenkins, K. Caines and A. Jackson, *Improving management in government: the next steps: Report to the Prime Minister*, HMSO, London 1988.

S. Jenkins, *Accountable to None: the Tory nationalisation of Britain*, Hamish Hamilton, London 1995.

J. Jones, 'NHS Doubles Pay-Bed Income', *The Independent*, 30 July 1993, p6.

S. Kuper, 'Dorrell to Slow NHS Reform', *Financial Times*, 20 July 1995, p18.

Labour Research Department, *Who Runs our Health Service? The occupational and political background of NHS Trust chairs and non-executive directors*, GMB, London 1994.

John G. Larson, 'The Role of Private Enterprise in Providing Health Care: Lessons of the American Experience', *National Westminster Bank Review*, November 1980, pp58-65.

D. S. Lees, 'The Economics of Health Services', *Lloyds Bank Review*, 56, 1960, pp26-40.

O. Letwin and J. Redwood, *Britain's Biggest Enterprise: Ideas for Radical Reform of the NHS*, Centre for Policy Studies, London 1988.

D.E. Light, 'Professionalism As a Countervailing Power', *Journal of Health Policy, Politics and Law*, 16, 1991, pp499-506.

C. M. Lindsay, *National Health Issues: The British Experience*, Hoffman La Roche Inc. Welwyn Garden City, 1980.

S. M. Lipset, *Political Man*, Heinemann, London 1963.

G. Mather, *Government by Contract*, Institute of Economic Affairs, London 1991.

A. Maynard, 'Developing the Health Care Market', *Economic Journal*, 101(408), September 1991, pp1277-1286.

R.S. McNamara and B. VanDeMark, *In Retrospect: The tragedy and lessons of Vietnam*, Times Books, New York 1995.

K. Miller and M. Steele, 'Employment Legislation: Thatcher and After', *Industrial Relations Journal*, 24, September 1993, pp224-236.

P. Minford, 'State Expenditure: A Study in Waste', *Economic Affairs*, Suppl. April-June 1984, ppi-xix.

Monopolies and Mergers Commission, *Services of Medical Practitioners CMND 582*, HMSO, London, March 1989.

J. Moore, 'Speech to American Health Care Conference', *DSS Press Release*, DHSS, 25 April 1988, p12.

G. Mulgan, 'Seven Maxims On the Future of Government', *Demos*, 7, 1995, pp9-11.

National Audit Office, *Value for Money Developments in the NHS: report by the Comptroller and Auditor General*, HMSO, London 1986.

V. Navarro, 'The Relevance of the U.S. Experience to the Reforms in the British National Health Service: The case of general practitioner fund holding', *Int. J Health Serv*, 21(3), 1991, pp381-388.

Newchurch & Company, *The 4th Newchurch Guide to NHS Trusts*, Newchurch and Company Ltd, London 1994.

NHS Executive, *The Operation of the Internal Market: local freedoms, national responsibilities*, Department of Health, London 1994.

NHS Management Executive, *Public Service, Private Finance ... putting private capital to work for the NHS*, NHSME, Leeds 1993.

D. Nichol, 'Changing the machinery: a perspective on market reforms in government', Speech by Sir Duncan Nichol to European Policy Forum, 30 March 1994.

Sir D. Nichol, 'Confronting the Issues', *The ISHM Network*, 3(1), 1996, p2.

OECD, *Health Policy Studies: 2. The Reform of Health Care: A Comparative Analysis of Seven OECD Countries*, Organisation for Economic Co-operation and Development, Paris 1992.

D. A. Perkins, 'Implementing the Managed Market: Considerations On the Introduction of Reforms in the UK.' *Hospital Topics*, 70(4), Fall 1992, pp32-36.

P. Pierson, *Dismantling the Welfare State?*, Cambridge University Press, Cambridge 1995.

A. Pike, 'In Need of Care and Attention', *Financial Times*, 30 July 1991, p15.

M. Prowse, 'The Isolation of the Individual', *Financial Times*, 4 May 1989, p11.

J. Randle, 'Beware of the NHS Trusts', *Independent Health Management*, June 1990, pp15,33.

G. Rayner, 'Cash Controversy That Still Keeps Its Spring', *Health Service Journal*, 99(5161), 27 July 1989, p906.

U. E. Reinhardt, 'Comment On the Jackson Hole Initiatives for a Twenty-First Century American Health Care System', *Health Economics*, 2, 1993, pp7-14.

C. E. Rosenberg, *The Care of Strangers: the rise of America's hospital system*, Basic Books, New York 1987.

B. Salter, 'Medicine and the State: Redefining the Concordat', *Public Policy and Administration*, 10(3), 1995, pp60-87.

M. Schrage, 'A Onetime Whiz Kid Transforms America's Health Care Debate', *Washington Post*, 3 December 1993, p1.

C. L. Schultze, *The Public Use of Private Interest*, The Brookings Institution, Washington, DC 1977.

R. M. Scleffler, 'Culture Versus Competition: The Reforms of the British National Health Service', *Journal of Public Health Care Policy*, 13(2), 1992, pp180-185.

R. Skidelsky, *The World after Communism: a polemic for our times*, Macmillan, London 1995.

R. Stevens, *In Sickness and in Wealth: American hospitals in the twentieth century*, Basic Books, New York 1989.

J. Tarshis, 'Why the Military Can't Get Figures Right', *American Heritage*, 37(2), February 1986, pp94-99.

A. Taylor, 'NHS Hospitals "Selling Land to Fund Repairs"', *Financial Times*, 13 October 1994, p11.

M. Terris, 'Budget Cutting and Privatization: The Threat to Health', *Public Health Policy*, 13(1), Spring 1992, pp27-41.

M. Thatcher, *The Downing Street Years*, HarperCollins, London 1993.

N. Timmins, 'Unions Being Excluded from Public Bodies', *The Independent*, 23 March 1995, p9.

J. P. Weiner and D. M. Ferriss, 'GP Budget Holding in the United

Kingdom: Learning from American HMOs', *Health Policy 1991*, 16(3), 1990, pp209-220.

P. Whiteley, P. Seyd and J. Richardson, *True Blues: The politics of Conservative Party membership*, Clarendon Press, Oxford 1994.

R. Whitney, *National Health Crisis: A Modern Solution*, Shepheard-Walwyn, London 1988.

D. Willets, 'The NHS Remedy - To Be Taken Internally', *The Guardian*, 1 February 1989a, p23.

D. Willets, *Reforming the Health Service*, Conservative Political Centre, London 1989b.

D. Willets, *The Opportunities for Private Funding in the NHS*, Social Market Foundation, London 1993.

HAS THE INTERNAL MARKET BEEN A SUCCESS? CONTRADICTIONS IN COMPETITION

James Munro

The only definite thing about radical reform is that you can never be sure how it will turn out. When Mrs Thatcher announced her NHS review in January 1988 - to the surprise of the opposition and her own cabinet ministers alike - nobody, least of all the prime minister, could have predicted the outcomes eight turbulent years later.

The proposals for reform were finally published in February 1989, as the White Paper *Working for Patients*. Politicians of both left and right recognised that here was an ambitious and ideologically-driven programme which, far from moving public services directly into the private sector, brought the language and structures of the market into the heart of the state itself. Not only did the programme entail considerable political risks, but the practical implications of reform were daunting. Even Conservative backbenchers expressed anxiety that the proposed timetable for the introduction of an internal market throughout the enormous bureaucracy of the health service by April 1991 was unfeasible and over-ambitious.

Kenneth Clarke, then secretary of state for health, pressed ahead undaunted. The timetable was, more or less, achieved. But far from being an end point, 1991 marked the beginning of a new period of transformation for health services in Britain, the logic of which has not yet wholly unravelled.

The purpose of this chapter is to review the contradictory objectives, structures and results of the internal market, the defining feature of the restructured NHS. While many of the changes which have taken place since the introduction of the internal market appear unpredictable and chaotic - an impression only reinforced by the apparent surprise of policymakers at each new and unanticipated problem - many of the likely consequences of the internal market were clearly predicted in advance, and were inherent in the structural changes proposed. Other characteristics have only become clear with the passage of time, and still others remain uncertain and unresearched.

THE CONTRADICTORY OBJECTIVES OF REFORM

On the face of it, the objectives of the NHS reforms were clear and unambiguous. In her foreword to *Working for Patients*, Mrs Thatcher made the government's purpose plain: 'We aim to extend patient choice, to delegate responsibility to where the services are provided and to secure the best value for money. All the proposals in this White Paper put the needs of patients first' (Department of Health, 1989).

It is easy to forget, given this bland statement of aims, that the immediate stimulus to the NHS review had been the 'bed crisis' of the winter of 1987/88, when intense media attention directed public concern towards lengthening waiting lists, bed shortages and staffing problems. The public perception at the time - as so often before and since - was that the NHS was chronically underfunded and desperately in need of increased spending in order to meet the demands being placed upon it (Butler, 1994). Although the prime minister announced her review of the NHS as a direct response to this political crisis over health care financing, it was not long before the search for alternatives to tax-based funding was quietly dropped (except by the plethora of right wing think-tanks seeking to advise ministers) in favour of an internal reorganisation which left the source and size of the NHS budget unchanged.

Of course, the continuation of taxation-based funding was unsurprising, since it had long been clear to most people - including Treasury economists who had investigated the alternatives in the early 1980s - that alternatives such as health care insurance were liable to greater administrative overheads and weaker control of overall costs. Nonetheless, a crisis fuelled by a public demand for an increase in health care spending had been defused by a response which promised no more cash, but which instead aimed to contain costs through promoting 'value for money'.

A second tension was evident in the gap between the political rhetoric of choice and the economic reality of rationing. The politicians spoke constantly in terms of an aggressive free-market individualism, which promised that, if only individuals could be given the freedom to choose for themselves, then the invisible hand of the market would ensure that health care provision would be as efficient as possible. The slogan that 'the money follows the patient' became a shorthand for all that would be best about the new system, a clear break with the old bureaucracy in which hospitals had had no economic incentive to improve the quality or efficiency of their services.

Yet, as long as the state was to be the ultimate source of finance for health care, the idea of increasing consumer choice was potentially, if not inevitably, incompatible with the aim of containing public sector spending. What would happen if patients were to exercise their new found power by choosing expensive or ineffective treatments? A system in which the balance between preventive and curative services, between low-tech and high-tech medicine, is determined by the aggregate of individual patient decisions, is plainly not one in which costs can easily be controlled or public health priorities pursued, as the experience of many countries has made clear. Even after the introduction of the internal market, it only slowly became clear to many that the newly empowered 'consumers' of health care were not the patients after all, but the health authority managers and fundholding doctors who purchased on their behalf.

It was often argued that both of these contradictions were more apparent than real, since the introduction of competitive discipline into the NHS would increase efficiency so much that the need for additional funding could be avoided. But a prerequisite for efficiency is effectiveness - a guarantee that what is being purchased actually works. This problem was barely addressed by the White Paper, which seemed to generate endless managerial debates about 'quality' but few about effectiveness, which appeared only in the guise of extending arrangements for medical audit, an activity defined by and confidential to the medical profession.

AN ALTERNATIVE POLICY PROGRAMME

An alternative path for health care reform, and arguably one just as likely to achieve high quality health care while containing costs, would have been based on the widespread promotion of effectiveness, rather than competition, as the stimulus to improved quality and efficiency. Indeed, a coherent argument for just such a programme was set out shortly after the publication of *Working for Patients* (Quam, 1989), and remains convincing. Clinical effectiveness is a prerequisite for 'value for money', whatever the system of financing, but Quam argued that the proposals in the White Paper made the possibilities for the successful promotion of clinical effectiveness *less* likely than before, because of the short-termism, fragmentation and secrecy that would result from market-led reform.

It soon became apparent to policymakers that they had no straightforward way to use competitive market relationships to promote effective, evidence-based care. Little importance, in policy terms, was placed on the promotion of effectiveness until well after the introduction of the internal market. Instead, an alternative 'clinical effectiveness reform' has gathered momentum in parallel with the structural reforms, lead initially by physicians, public health specialists and academics, and taken up only belatedly by managers. Currently, this takes a number of forms, including the 'evidence-based medicine' movement, the Cochrane Collaboration, the NHS Centre for Reviews and Dissemination and local projects aimed at translating between the worlds of management, research and clinical practice, such as the FACTS project in Sheffield and the GRiPP project in Oxfordshire.

THE CONTRADICTORY STRUCTURES OF REFORM

We generally speak of the internal market in the NHS as if

there were only one. But contradictory ends require contradictory means. In keeping with the government's desire both to control the costs of health care and to promote increased choice for 'consumers', two distinct and wholly incompatible market structures were created. These differ by virtue of the characteristics of the purchaser of health care, and have been termed type I and type II markets (Mullen, 1989). In both, the providers of care are public sector hospitals and community services, as well as commercial and voluntary sector organisations.

The type I market is based on a 'needs-led' model of health care purchasing. In this market, the purchaser is a health authority, acting on behalf of a geographically defined resident population. The basis for purchasing decisions is, in very general terms, taken to be the utilitarian one of maximising the 'health gain' which can be achieved for the population as a whole from a fixed budget. The authority is charged with the responsibility of undertaking 'health needs assessments' to determine both the state of health of its population and the services which are required to meet the needs so identified. This process requires evidence on the effectiveness and cost-effectiveness of all possible interventions so as to maximise the potential health gain which can be achieved.

By contrast, the type II market is based on a 'demand-led' model. Here, the market exists between providers and those primary care doctors who have chosen to hold their own budget for hospital and community care - the GP fundholders. The characteristics of the GP purchaser are quite different from those of the health authority. There is no requirement to assess the health needs of a population, nor even necessarily of the list of enrolled patients, but only to respond to individual demand as it presents itself in the consulting room. Nor is there any requirement to assess the likely effectiveness of different possible strategies for prevention and treatment, but only, ultimately, to act as an agent for the individual patient in arranging for care which will meet their needs and satisfy their preferences.

In this market there is also the possibility, because a GP's patient population is based on mutual agreement rather than place of residence, that individuals may choose to change GP on the basis of their fundholding status or purchasing policies. Similarly, GPs may choose to remove patients from their lists or refuse to accept new patients if they look as if they will be heavy users of the GP's fund. While there have been a steady trickle of anecdotal examples of such 'risk selection', no systematic published evidence on this issue yet exists in Britain (Dixon and Glennerster, 1995). However, it would be surprising to find that the same incentives which generate this perverse outcome in other systems do not do so when applied here (Glaser, 1993).

The devolution of budgets to primary care physicians, in the form of GP fundholding, therefore creates not only a market between fundholders and hospitals - a provider market - but also the possibility of market-like behaviour between patients and their GPs - a purchaser market, in which patients really do become customers. Such a development is likely to be encouraged both by the liberalisation of practice advertising and by the simplification of the procedures for changing doctors, and would be expected to lead to increasingly overt competition between fundholders for patients - particularly, of course, for those patients least likely to need care.

Mullen has described the confusion which accompanied the policymaking debate over the NHS reforms, since these two distinct market structures were created without any clear understanding of their quite different implications for efficiency, equity, choice and cost control (Mullen, 1989). The type I (health authority) model allows a high degree of control over both costs and the ability to promote priorities for health care expenditure. Health authorities purchasing for defined populations are able, at least potentially, to identify and address public health priorities, the interests of different population groups, the possibility of unmet (and perhaps unexpressed) need, and the promotion of equity of access to health care. However, this strong population perspective comes at the price of freedom of choice for patients and their GPs, who are supposed to keep within the bounds of the contracts agreed on their behalf by the planners.

The type II (fundholder) model offers far greater freedom

of choice to GPs and, in theory, to patients. Practices negotiate for acute and community trusts to provide them with services which are cheaper, quicker or more convenient than before, without the layers of bureaucracy entailed by health authority purchasing. The other side of this coin is that, while emphasising responsiveness to patients, practices have no need to consider the community beyond their list, although many do. Not only is the rationale for purchasing quite different, but the segment of population covered by each practice is so small that, for anything but the most common conditions, the demand for services will fluctuate wildly from year to year.

The two purchasers of the NHS and their respective markets seem to have come to represent the competing political ideologies driving British health care reform. On the one hand, the health authority embodies the rational planning instincts of those who seek to contain health care costs and maximise efficiency in the use of resources, and on the other GP fundholders embody the aspirations of those who would achieve efficiency - and consumer choice - through the promotion of as free a market as politically possible. The tensions evident in the objectives of reform have been carried through into the structures.

THE CONTRADICTORY OUTCOMES OF REFORM

No simple verdict as to the 'success' of the reforms can be delivered, not least because the criteria by which success might be judged are themselves contentious. Further, as argued above, the reform programme sought to achieve outcomes which are likely to be mutually contradictory, at least so long as the NHS remains publicly funded.

Nonetheless, it is possible to attempt some judgement of whether the reformers succeeded in their own terms, that is, in promoting competition, increasing efficiency and extending patient choice. In doing so, it is worth bearing in mind that we should not allow the choices we make about the organisation of public services to be determined simply by technical matters such as waiting times, activity levels and efficiency indices, as if these were the only things we valued. The nature and quality of the organisational and personal relationships which are fostered by the health service are equally, or more, important, a point to which I return below.

Given the contradictory aims of reform, it is not surprising that the outcomes have frequently been at odds with the brave new world envisaged by the reformers. Far from creating a system in which bureaucracy melts away, providers freely compete for business and patients are always right, the post-reform NHS has generated new battalions of managers, new layers of regulatory control and a fragmented service in which patients remain confused and powerless.

Managing the market: competition or regulation?

The reforms were intended to secure increased efficiency through competition between providers in a market in which, as in any high street, prices are published and are visible to all the players in the system. Indeed, it has been explicit Department of Health policy that providers should make public their tariffs to encourage such competition. The picture painted at the outset of the reforms was of a market in which purchasers - health authorities and fundholders alike - would 'shop around' for the cheapest, quickest or best quality care.

In reality, as Diane Dawson has convincingly argued, the NHS internal market has none of the characteristics of a retail market, and stubbornly refuses to behave like one (Dawson, 1994). It has much more in common with an 'industrial market', in which there are few purchasers and providers, the product is complex and infinitely variable, and providers carry a high proportion of fixed costs. The result is that packages of care - and prices - are negotiated privately between purchasers and providers, and relationships are likely to be long term. In itself, as Dawson suggests, this is not necessarily harmful to the efficiency of the market. In practice, though, the lack of fixed and observable prices irritates the market regulator, the Department of Health, and may, in effect, render impossible the health authority's theoretical task of maximising the 'health gain' achievable from limited resources.

There are other good economic reasons to suppose that the market, even as it 'matures', will not behave as planned. For example, as health authorities move away from simple block contracting and towards more specific contracting arrangements, the challenge of negotiating contractual forms which balance the financial incentives for providers with the desire of the health authority to get the maximum from its resources becomes ever more difficult (Chalkley and Malcolmson, 1995). Agree too high a price, or for too many patients, and the purchaser wastes public money. Too low a price, or for too few patients, and hospitals lower their quality standards or stop treating patients before the year end. Set the contract for too short a period (and many managers are now arguing that one year is too short) and risk the 'ratchet effect' and the 'hold up effect' (both discussed in Chalkley and Malcolmson, 1995) which generate perverse incentives for providers to under-perform. Set the contract for a longer period, and lose the supposed benefits of competitive contracting as providers allow quality to slip or costs to rise.

It would be difficult enough if it really were a competitive market. But while they established radical new structures intended to encourage competitive behaviour, the NHS management executive also drew the lines of regulation and monitoring so tightly that no real competition has been allowed to emerge. Of course, in very many parts of the country competition was always wholly unrealistic because providers, especially community services, are effectively local monopolies. Yet even in London and other large cities which might actually be able to support a competitive provider market, regulation has been as tight - or tighter - than anywhere else. The NHSE has constantly intervened to impose or refuse mergers between providers, to prevent health authorities from moving their contracts away from under-performing hospitals which might become non-viable as a result (Le Grand, 1994), to regulate capital borrowing by trusts and to disallow cross-subsidies between services within the same provider. Indeed, in some districts with two or more large providers, health authorities have come to local agreements with hospitals that designate each as the 'lead provider' in particular services, effectively neutralising any possibility of competition.

Market theorists have moved on from straightforward competition to the notion of 'contestability' as a way of resolving this problem (Robinson and Le Grand, 1995). It may be enough just to have the threat of competition, they argue, for providers to improve their performance. While this may be true as long as the threat seems real, one could not continue to use 'contestability' as a policy instrument if the threat was never likely to become reality. The idea of contestability is weakened further by the observation that the high level of start-up investment required poses a significant barrier to new providers entering the health care market. In many places, even contestability is unrealistic.

The picture of 'managed competition' which emerges from the post-reform NHS is one in which management seems to heavily outweigh competition. While the Department of Health continues to talk in terms of 'the process of devolution stimulated by the NHS reforms', the reality is that political and managerial power in the health service have become more centralised (Paton, 1992). This trend will undoubtedly be consolidated by the transformation of the former regional health authorities into arms of the Department of Health. Indeed, one political commentator describes the outcome of the reforms as a 'neo-nationalisation' (Jenkins, 1995).

Given such developments, it is natural to ask whether the supposed benefits of competition could possibly emerge from a market in which almost no competition seems actually to exist. Might we have ended up with a system in which we are paying for all the costs of competition - which include fragmentation, confusion, perverse incentives and erosion of a public service ethic, as well as the purely financial costs - yet getting none of the benefits?

Financial costs of the market

In judging the reforms against the criterion of securing 'the best value for money', we have to make some assessment of the financial costs of establishing and running the new system. In the reform bill which went before Parliament in 1989, the government put its estimate of the overhead required to operate an internal market in the NHS at £217m per year. This sum was to cover an increase in management at all levels (£155m), payments to health authority members (£10.5m), administration of the fundholding scheme (£15.6m) and new information technology (£3.3m).

The real costs of establishing the reforms are difficult to estimate, but are certainly much higher. Even the official implementation figures are well in excess of the initial estimates: £79m in 1989-90, £306m in 1990-91, £383m in 1991-92 (Dorrell, 1991). Additional start-up costs must be added in respect of fundholding and the establishment of capital asset registers, among other things (Petchey, 1993). As a rough and ready estimate, the NHS Consultants Association has estimated, from official figures for 1992-93, that the overall costs of administration of the NHS amount to 11.6 per cent of total health service expenditure (National Health Service Consultants Association, 1994), contrasting with pre-reform figures of around 5 to 6 per cent of total costs.

What of the costs associated with the day-to-day operation of any marketplace - the transaction costs? Unfortunately, there is little information available, and what there is relates mainly to the costs of fundholding rather than health authority contracting. While health authorities have dealt mainly in block contracts, it is likely that transaction costs will not have gone far beyond that which would have been spent in traditional planning mode, though if contract negotiations increase in specificity and in number, then costs will rise accordingly. Extra-contractual referrals - which result when a patient is referred to provider with whom the health authority does not already have a contract - may pose a more significant cost to purchasers. One director of public health said of his experience of the first three months of dealing with ECRs: 'What is absolutely certain is that we are spending a lot of management and clinical time making decisions on a relatively small number of patients.' (Williamson, 1991). Others commented that 'dealing with extra-contractual referrals will always take a disproportionate amount of time because it involves a large number of cases, each handled individually' (Ghodse and Rawaf, 1991). Indeed, even after three years experience of dealing with ECRs, one commissioning manager estimated that ECRs were costing the NHS in her district almost £0.3m annually simply for the administrative processes necessary (Ghodse, 1995). She predicted that the problem must inevitably worsen.

A number of estimates have been made of the additional administrative costs incurred by the fundholding scheme. Petchey calculates that the operating costs of fundholding in 1993-94 amounted to £66.6m or 3.5 per cent of the total fundholding budget, and adds that £165m was paid to fundholders between 1990 and 1995 for managerial support (Petchey, 1995). A survey carried out by *Fundholding* magazine suggested that the annual cost of managing fundholding might reach £80,000 per practice (Davies, 1995), and even a riposte by two fundholders conceded a figure of around £60,000 was realistic (Morris and Armstrong, 1995).

It is clear that the transaction costs of fundholding are considerably higher than those of health authority commissioning. For example, Davies estimates practice-based management costs at about 6 per cent of an average fundholder's practice budget. This contrasts with the management costs of a health authority, estimated to be about 1.7 per cent (Davies, 1995). If the total number of fundholders increases and the services covered by the fund are extended, then inevitably such costs will become a significant charge on the overall NHS budget.

If one aim of the reforms was to reduce NHS bureaucracy, then on this count they would have to be judged a spectacular failure. Inevitably, the information and accounting tasks associated with the introduction of a market have resulted in an enormous increase in the number of health service managers and administrative and clerical staff. The most public and therefore most controversial expression of the cost of the market has been in the almost exponential rise in health service managers. Between 1988 and 1993 the number of general and senior managers rose from 1,240 to 20,010 (Department of Health, 1994). Public concern over this apparently burgeoning bureaucracy prompted repeated departmental protestations that much of the increase could be explained in terms of the reclassification of nursing and administrative posts as managerial ones. Nonetheless, there is no denying that a large proportion of the increase is a genuine expansion in managerial numbers, estimated by one analyst as an additional 1,700 managers over the period 1991-94 (Appleby, 1995).

All of these additional costs which result from the creation of the internal market pose an important, and as yet unanswered, challenge to the claim that the reforms have secured 'best value for money'. It is at least possible that the old, bureaucratic way of doing things was, in fact, more efficient after all. Some theoretical support for this idea comes from the work of the economist Oliver Williamson, who has examined the conditions under which management hierarchies are more efficient than market relationships (discussed in Robinson and Le Grand, 1995). In the light of this work, it is certainly arguable that the characteristics of health care provision are such that the attempt to replace hierarchical with market-like structures will lead to a fall in efficiency.

Increased NHS efficiency?
What evidence do we have that the efficiency of the NHS has improved as a result of the reforms? The first point to note is that NHS activity increased remarkably during the 1980s, a period during which economic theorists would have us believe that no incentives existed to improve performance. For example, the average length of stay for acute medicine fell 29 per cent, and for acute surgery 13 per cent. The average cost per inpatient stay fell, in real terms, by 10 per cent. Hospitals treated 16 per cent more in-patients, 19 per cent more emergency cases and carried out 73 per cent more day surgery in 1989 than in 1980 (Light, 1995).

These gains were achieved under the old regime of bureaucracy and planning, without a market in sight. So did the reformed NHS do even better? Predictably, before the first year of the internal market had ended the NHS Management

Executive had claimed 'even better value for money' as a result of the restructuring, citing improvements in hospital admissions and waiting lists (NHSME, 1992). Yet, as Klein pointed out, the figures were open to interpretation, since the management executive predicted in-patient activity to rise faster than in the previous three years - but more slowly than the average over the previous decade (Klein, 1992). A detailed critique of the statistics, which pointed to existing trends, changes in data collection and the important shift from counting hospital discharges and deaths to 'finished consultant episodes' (FCEs) as additional explanations for the figures, concluded that the data 'fail to support Duncan Nichol's claim that the changes ... are leading to ... better value for money' (Radical Statistics Health Group, 1992).

Others have accepted that activity did increase substantially during 1991-92, but point to the remarkable increase in NHS funding during the years 1990 to 1992 (compared with virtually zero real growth during the 1980s) as a sufficient explanation (Petchey, 1993). Many of the subsequent claims made in the stream of press releases and 'good news' annual reports which have issued from the Department of Health and the NHS Executive have been comprehensively refuted by academic statisticians (Radical Statistics Health Group, 1995).

Extending patient choice?

A further result at variance with the promises of the reformers has been the effect of reform on the choices available to individual service users. For example, in the year that *Working for Patients* was published, then secretary of state for health Kenneth Clarke promised: 'In order to bring more choice to patients, GPs and hospitals will be required to tell patients what their range of services will be' (Clarke, 1989).

The rhetoric that 'the money would follow the patient' was rapidly replaced, as might have been predicted, by the patient following the money in the block contracts which health authorities negotiate. The reforms provided users with no means, either as individuals or collectively, to influence either service providers or purchasers directly, and the rapidly increasing fragmentation and complexity of the system following the introduction of the purchaser-provider split made talk of a 'seamless service' sound increasingly remote from reality. This was reflected in the actual experiences of service users. For example, a 1993 survey of consumer views of the NHS found that the proportion of people experiencing difficulty arranging in-patient hospital treatment doubled between 1989 and 1993 (National Consumer Council, 1993).

That the reforms have failed in their aim of 'empowering the consumer' has not been lost on right-wing commentators, as one might expect. John Spiers, formerly a high profile health authority chair and now health policy adviser to the Social Market Foundation, remarks on the post-reform NHS as 'a culture in which patients have been given the apparent status of consumers whose wants should be met, but without any power of sanction' (Spiers, 1995). Noisy demands from the right for a 'real empowerment' of patients through extending private health insurance or introducing patient voucher schemes can be expected to intensify.

Low trust relationships
The tight regulation of the provider market may, as argued above, have effectively prevented the emergence of a competitive marketplace, but it has not prevented various undesirable features of market relationships from appearing in the health service, well described by Harrison and Lachmann (1996) as 'low trust relationships'. The reformed health service is fast becoming a place in which 'everything must be defined, documented, formalised and transformed into a quasi-contractual relationship ... such implications of low trust are likely to be self-fulfilling' (Harrison and Lachmann, 1996).

The insidious spread of such low trust relationships will gradually erode the spirit of altruism which has often brought people into the public services to begin with. But the impact of the organisational fragmentation at the heart of the reforms has been not just to make the NHS a less caring place to work, but to introduce a range of perverse incentives which make it harder to promote the desired technical ends of efficiency and effectiveness. As usual, these results were predictable from the start (Harrison, 1991).

There is enough evidence available to suggest that perverse incentives are not simply theoretical, but are having a real effect on the day-to-day running of the NHS. For example, one would predict that a system in which providers are paid according to a notional unit of activity - the 'finished consultant episode' or FCE - would have an incentive to manipulate the system to generate maximum FCEs at no additional cost, an example of gaming. It did not take long for both anecdotal (Anonymous, 1992) and systematic (Clarke and McKee, 1992) reports to appear confirming the existence of 'FCE inflation'.

The attempt to manage a service through contracts and performance targets leads to a second form of perversity, known as goal displacement, in which the wider purpose of the service is ignored in the rush to meet the targets set. The government's choice of waiting times as the highest profile target against which the success of the reforms would be measured has generated just such an outcome. Patients waiting over a year have been treated willy-nilly, without regard to the urgency or otherwise of their condition compared to that of patients waiting under a year, to the concern of the clinicians who listed them for surgery. Worse, the scramble to bring the longest queues to below 12 months has, on the one hand, prevented new patients from being added to the list, while on the other, patients have been in effect removed from lists or encouraged to seek treatment elsewhere (Brindle, 1996). Somehow this is thought to represent better management.

A third perverse incentive, adverse selection, has been referred to above, and has arisen mainly in connection with fundholding. While no systematic evidence yet exists that fundholders add or remove patients from their lists according to risk, there is the widespread (but officially denied) preference given by trusts to the patients of fundholders, in particular for elective surgery. To the extent that the most deprived areas are less likely to be served by a fundholding practice, the result is in effect an adverse selection by the hospitals against the poor. Further, in some areas the incentive to do elective over emergency surgical work seems likely to lead to a deteriorating quality of care for patients who need it the most.

Finally, cost shifting results when one organisation attempts to protect its budget by shunting the care, and costs, of a patient to some other part of the system. Cost shifting has long been a feature of the boundaries between health and social care, and between primary and secondary care, which predated the reforms. The introduction of budgets in primary care has introduced the new incentive for fundholders to increase the use their patients make of A&E departments (which is not a charge on the fund) in preference to elective admission (which is). Although emergency admissions seem to have risen steadily in recent years, causing fevered discussions about possible causes, nobody seems to have examined the possibility of cost shifting in any depth.

The problem of legitimacy

The issue of local democratic control of health services has remained unresolved since the inception of the NHS in 1948, when Labour bowed to pressure from the medical profession and decided against the 'local authority option'. It was no surprise that a government of the right with a deep distrust of local authorities, coming to reform the NHS 40 years later, would do nothing to redress this. Indeed, the government argued that health authorities (HAs) needed to 'slim down' and operate in a businesslike way, and this was offered as the justification for removing the last vestiges of local democratic representation from HA membership.

But in separating purchasing from the provision of health care, the reformers have paradoxically drawn attention to the problem of political legitimacy in health care decision-making and, far from depoliticising the health service, have pushed its formerly faceless bureaucrats firmly into the public domain. The transformation of the work of authorities from organising and managing services to agreeing priorities for public spending on health services means that its role has changed from a managerial to a representative one. At the same time, they have cast off any last element of representative composition. On what basis, then, can HAs lay claim to this much trumpeted new status as 'champions of the people' if the people are nowhere represented?

The solution to this crisis of legitimacy has been sought, as it usually is, through vigorously promoting a claim for technical expertise in place of a popular mandate. Such expertise takes a number of forms, from the epidemiological to the economic, from 'listening to local voices' to 'evidence-based purchasing'. As the people are disaggregated from being an electorate into a series of 'focus groups', so a complex statistical re-aggregation of their individual choices, preferences and valuations of health states becomes the basis for policy. In the new NHS, health authorities have been forced to re-invent themselves as the expert advocates of need, effectiveness, efficiency and equity. But in presenting priority setting and the allocation of public funds as an essentially technical problem, the NHS not only disenfranchises people but simultaneously denies that it has done so (Munro, 1993).

CONTINUITIES IN THE REFORM PROCESS

I have argued that the outcomes of the reforms of the NHS have produced a range of unintended and contradictory results. Nonetheless, there are also strong continuities in the Conservatives' transformation of health care which should not be neglected. Briefly, I would suggest the following are among them.

First, the role of private finance in the provision of public health services has steadily increased. This process began in the early 1980s with compulsory competitive tendering for hospital ancillary services, and has gathered pace since then, in a variety of forms. The most recent example of this is the Private Finance Initiative, introduced in 1992 (Pollock, 1995; Whitfield, 1996).

Hand in hand with this, the boundary between public and private sector has become so blurred as to be virtually unrecognisable. The income of NHS trusts from private patients rose 63 per cent in the first three years of the 'internal' market (Brindle, 1995), private provision has virtually replaced long-term care by the NHS (Pollock, 1994), and even some NHS clinical services are now supplied by private companies.

Second, political accountability for the allocation of public funds within the NHS has been weakened. Since 1948, accountability has existed only centrally through the secretary of state for health, who is accountable to Parliament. While this formal accountability has not been changed by the reforms, its exercise in practice by MPs has become more difficult. The Department of Health habitually deflects searching questions on local NHS matters with stock replies along the lines of 'this information is not collected centrally' or 'this is a matter for the local health authority'. National accountability through Parliament has become, at best, tenuous.

Yet local accountability is, as I argued above, non-existent. Further, the introduction of GP fundholding has raised concerns over the financial probity of the scheme, since fundholders, as other GPs, are small independent businesses which contract with the NHS. They are not obliged to spend the whole of their fund on patient care, and in the four years of the scheme have collectively built up a large surplus. Much of this has gone into improving the practice premises, which are owned by the doctors themselves.

Third, the role of the state in relation to health services is changing from that of provider to that of regulator. Of course, this has been a characteristic in very many spheres of state activity over the past two decades, including local government services, transport policy, the major utilities, telecommunications, and so on. That this global trend has only recently impinged on the British NHS only serves to underline how resilient (or perhaps popular) that institution has been (Munro, 1990)

Fourth, there has been a consistent trend to challenge the autonomy of health professionals through a range of mechanisms, including increased managerial power, new contracts and job plans for consultants, attempts to introduce performance-related pay, medical audit, continuing professional education, clinical protocols and the like, hospital (and possibly clinician) league tables, and a range of financial incentives in primary care activity, such as vaccination and cervical cytology (Harrison, 1994). This is another facet of the paradoxical centralisation of power which has resulted from 'decentralising' reforms.

Overall, the picture is of the progressive privatisation of all elements of health care, alongside the reduction in the state's role except as market regulator. It is entirely consistent with this that public accountability and control over local health services diminish still further. After all, the logic of the market is that individual 'consumers' exert their influence only through personal purchasing or insurance decisions, but not through any direct influence on the providers.

Of course, this is the context in which the reforms ultimately make the greatest sense. They were never simply a technical exercise in securing 'value for money', but were one element in a much more ambitious restructuring of the welfare state as a whole, according to a right-wing social agenda which aims to diminish the role of the state and the power of professionals as it increases the opportunities for private capital and individual choice. The continuities I outline above suggest that, against these criteria, the creation of an internal market has taken the NHS a long way towards these goals.

References

Anonymous, 'Gain Without Pain', *Health Service Journal*, 30 January 1992.

Appleby J., 'Managers: in the ascendancy?' *Health Service Journal*, 21 September 1995, pp32-3.

Brindle D., 'Queries over leap in NHS paybed income', *Guardian*, 4 May 1995.

Brindle D., 'Row over NHS targets: health body aiming to remove patients to meet time guarantee', *Guardian*, 31 January 1996.

Butler J., 'Origins and Early Development', *Evaluating the NHS Reforms*, King's Fund Institute, London 1994.

Clarke A. and McKee M., 'The Consultant Episode: an unhelpful measure', *BMJ*, 305, 1992, pp1307-8.

Davies J., 'How much does the scheme cost?' *Fundholding*, 4(2), 1995, pp22-4.

Dawson D., 'Costs and prices in the internal market: markets vs the NHS Management Executive Guidelines', Centre for Health Economics Discussion Paper No. 115, University of York, York 1994.

Department of Health, Welsh Office, Scottish Home and Health Department and Northern Ireland Office (1989), *Working for Patients*, Cm 555, HMSO, London.

Department of Health, Statistical Bulletin 1994/11, HMSO 1994.

Dixon J. and Glennerster H., 'What do we know about fundholding in general practice?' *BMJ*, 311, 1995, pp727-30.

Dorrell S., NHS Reforms, House of Commons Official Report, Hansard 6 December 1991, pp200: col245 (No 27).

Ghodse B., 'Extra-contractual referrals: safety valve or administrative paperchase?' *BMJ*, 310, 1995, pp1573-6.

Ghodse B. and Rawaf S., 'Extra-contractual referrals in the first three months of NHS reforms', *BMJ*, 303, 1991, pp497-9.

Glaser WA., 'The competition vogue and its outcomes', *Lancet*, 341, 1993, pp805-12.

Harrison S., 'From Here to Perversity', *Health Matters*, 7, 1991.

Harrison S. and Lachmann PJ., *Towards a high trust NHS: proposals for minimally invasive reform*, Institute for Public Policy Research, London 1996.

Harrison S. and Pollitt C., *Controlling health professionals: the future of work and organisation in the NHS*, Open University Press, Buckingham 1994.

Jenkins S., *Accountable to None: the Tory nationalisation of Britain*, Hamish Hamilton, 1995.

Klein R., 'NHS Reforms: the first six months', *BMJ*, 304, 1992, pp199-200.

Le Grand J., 'Internal market rules OK', *BMJ*, 309, pp1596-7.

Light DW., 'Homo economicus: escaping the traps of managed competition', *European J Public Health*, 5, 1995, pp145-54.

Morris R.and Armstrong M., 'Do not overestimate the scheme's costs', *Fundholding*, 4(4), 1995, p13.

Mullen P., 'Health and the internal market: implications of the White Paper', Discussion paper no. 25, University of Birmingham health services management centre, Birmingham 1989.

Munro J., 'Post-modern Medicine', *Medical World*, Autumn 1990, pp20-21.

Munro J., 'Why health economists are economical with the truth', *Health Care Analysis*, 1(2), 1993, pp197-9.

National Health Service Consultants Association, *In Practice: the NHS market*. NHSCA, Banbury 1994.

National Health Service Management Executive, *The NHS Reforms: the first six months*, Department of Health, London 1992.

Paton C., 'Firm Control', *Health Service Journal*, 6 August 1992, pp20-22.

Petchey R., 'NHS internal market 1991-2: towards a balance sheet', *BMJ*, 306, 1993, pp699-701.

Petchey R., 'General practitioner fundholding: weighing the evidence', *Lancet*, 346, 1995, pp1139-42.

Pollock A. M., 'The creeping privatisation of community care', *Health Matters*, (20), Winter 1994, pp9-11.

Pollock A. M., 'The NHS goes private', *Lancet*, 346, 1995, pp683-84.

Quam L., 'Improving clinical effectiveness in the NHS: an alternative to the White Paper', BMJ 1989; 299: pp448-50.

Radical Statistics Health Group, 'NHS Reforms: The First Six Months - proof of progress or a statistical smokescreen?' *BMJ*, 304, 1992, pp705-9.

Radical Statistics Health Group, 'NHS "indicators of success": what do they tell us?' *BMJ*, 310, 1995, pp1045-50.

Robinson R. and Le Grand J., 'Contracting and the purchaser-provider split' in *Implementing planned markets in health care: balancing social and economic responsibility*, Saltman R. B. and von Otter C. (eds), Open University Press, Buckingham 1995.

Spiers J., *The Invisible Hospital and the Secret Garden*, Radcliffe Medical Press, Oxford 1995.

Whitfield D., 'The private finance initiative', *Health Matters*, 24, Winter 1996.

Williamson J. D., 'Dealing with extra-contractual referrals', *BMJ*, 303, 1991, pp499-504.

TOWARDS A PRIMARY CARE-LED
NHS?

Steve Iliffe

The United Kingdom has been unusual in providing universal free health care in which access to hospital services is largely controlled by general practitioners who look after a defined list of patients of all ages, having responsibility for their care 24 hours a day throughout the year. It is generally considered that this gatekeeper function has contributed to the relatively low cost of the National Health Service, which by the late 1980s was spending less than half as much per head of population on health care as the USA, and only two thirds of the amount spent in Sweden (Pereira Gray, 1991), although the cost containment effect of general practice is probably exaggerated by the profession's political advocates.[1]

Recent Conservative administrations have favoured a 'primary care led NHS', and it has promoted the growth of 'fundholding' - through which general practitioners have a fund for purchasing specialist, secondary care - as a concrete example of this. The impetus for this change of orientation from a hospital-centred health service to one based on general practice has come from political ideologies rather than from the potential inherent within the existing structure. Fundholding has been promoted as a mechanism for kick-starting the market in health care, and has now become an end in itself as a professional ideology that over-values general practice sees, at last, its opportunity to dominate policy development. Nevertheless, a primary care led NHS is unlikely to emerge in the form envisaged by the Conservative government because changes within the general practitioner workforce and the changing relationship between primary and secondary care are pushing developments in the opposite direction.

THE BACKGROUND

General practice has been seen as a lever for the introduction of a market in medical care because general practitioners have never been part of the NHS in the way that hospital doctors, community nurses or most other professional and non-professional workers are. Most NHS staff have always been employees, but general practice as a whole has been run as a contracted out service ever since 1948, for complex historical reasons, and general practitioners have been independent of the command-and-control structure of the health service. To the extent that general practice developed successfully during the 1970s and 1980s, it demonstrated that a contracted-out service could provide a population with basic medical care, and therefore could act as a precedent for contracting hospital care out to semi-autonomous Trusts. Its potential role as a catalyst for the development of a market, however, derives from the political belief (unsupported by evidence) that more independence acquired through adopting a purchasing role would lead to more efficiency in the provision of medical care.

The independence of British general practitioners from the NHS management structure is not as great as that of, say, German doctors from their insurance organisations, but it is still very real. This independence is easy to understand if viewed as a form of public sector franchising. Franchising is an economic system in which a central organisation lends its trading name and logistic support to locally-owned outlets whose proprietors take the financial risks of trading (Stanworth & Smith, 1991).

In the NHS the Department of Health acts as a franchisor, getting a network of primary care outlets - general practices - at low cost and minimal risk to itself. These practices are staffed by a committed and relatively stable workforce of doctors who have extensive knowledge of both local populations and their problems, and of local medical and social resources.

General practitioners functioning as franchisees get protection against risk through:

♦ generous financial support (essentially, an interest-free loan plus improvement grants) that subsidises the building or conversion of premises;

♦ a basic (but small) salary that is paid to them regardless of their workload;

♦ the organisation of a registered patient population for which the doctors are paid on a per capita basis, again independently of actual workload;

♦ reimbursement of nursing and clerical staff wages;

♦ predictable and reliable cash flows, NHS index-linked pensions and sickness insurance;

♦ and other forms of financial support like favourable business taxation.

The franchisees also get some assistance in practice management while retaining local autonomy and everyday control of their activity.

Franchising can be a form of organisation in which success is cloned rapidly at limited cost to the central management. This may be one reason why the government sought, through the 1991 NHS reform, to shift hospitals and community services onto a franchise basis, in the shape of self-governing Trusts that had to compete within the managed market for NHS money instead of receiving a planned allocation. However, the natural history of franchising has features that general practitioners did not appear to understand before the beginning of the 1990s (Stanworth & Smith, 1991).

A franchise chain selling, say, pizzas wants to ensure that its product is the same in Brighton as it is in Birmingham. The same is true of a medical franchise funded by government money. To ensure that products or services are of standard quality, franchisors seek increasing control over their franchisees as time passes, especially when the outlet network enlarges and becomes more complex in its activities. Unilateral modification of contracts by franchisors then occurs, and the independence of the franchisee is eroded by increasingly specific contractual obligations, so that a point can sometimes be reached where the franchisee has all the responsibilities of an employee but none of the rights. In its later stages franchising can become a launch strategy for a qualitatively new industry, first allowing the rapid development of services which then become too complex and too costly for local entrepreneurs to buy into and manage, with the result that the franchisor imposes its own management structure.

The new contract for GPs imposed despite intense professional opposition in 1990, was an example of the unilateral tightening of franchisee contracts by a franchisor seeking standardisation of an increasingly diverse range of services, and with hindsight seems an almost inevitable consequence of the growth and development that occurred in general practice in the 1980s (see below). However, the co-incidence of the new contract for general practice and the NHS reforms of 1991 introduced a new dimension to franchising: fundholding.

THE INTERNAL MARKET AND GENERAL PRACTICE

The 1990 GP contract was part of a broader market reform of the NHS which included plans that would allow larger general practices to hold their own budgets in order to buy a defined range of services from specialists working in hospitals - the fundholding option. In effect this meant that some general practice franchisees could opt to extend their local autonomy even further, at the price of running greater risks, in order to catalyse the internal market in the NHS, where both hospitals and community services were being shifted from a centrally managed structure onto the franchise basis pioneered in general practice.

While a few general practitioners embraced the concept of fundholding with enthusiasm at the outset (Houghton, 1993), there was widespread concern about the possible adverse effects of fundholding for practices and patients, including fears that equity of access to services would be undermined and that the administrative structure required would become a considerable extra burden for busy practices that few were in a position to carry (Leese & Smedley, 1989). Concern at the threat to equity remains unabated, but the administrative overload has been circumvented by cash support for investment in management skills and information technology, so that an increasing number of general practitioners have been drawn towards fundholding.

However, despite the expansion of fundholding to cover 40 per cent of the population by 1995, this innovation has become a policy problem for the National Health Service. First hailed as a success (Glennerster, Owens & Matsaganis, 1992), it now seems dogged by limited advantages, high costs and unintended consequences, of which the greatest is the assault on equitable provision of health care.

So far the only area where fundholders have a demonstrable advantage over traditional franchisees is in reducing prescribing costs (Bradlow & Coulter, 1993; Maxwell, Heaney, Howie & Noble, 1993). This was a government objective, but success in cost containment tells us nothing about either the quality of care, which may decline as medicine costs are cut, or the long term economic costs of short-term savings on prescribing, which may be considerable. (Teeling-Smith, 1992) Since medication costs are being transferred to patients through higher prescription charges and a widening range of over-the-counter (OTC) medicines, the likely end result of downward pressure on prescribing costs is greater expenditure on medication by those who can afford them, and less use of medication by those who cannot.

The economic costs of fundholding are substantial. They include both open costs like management fees, subsidies for computerisation and administrative costs in the practice from the billing and contract review processes, as well as hidden costs like staff time in Family Health Service Authorities, Trust hospitals and the Audit Commission (a government agency that investigates the efficiency of public organisations). The opportunity costs of developing fundholding are not debated, but diverting resources to already well-endowed shire county practices to enhance their purchasing power while not spending development money on primary care services in deprived areas (outside London) is an assault on equity. The political costs may be equally significant, given the damage done to equity by fundholders buying speedier treatment for their patients - 'fast tracking' - which appears impossible to prove but is accepted as fact whenever fundholders and provider units speak off the record.

Fundholding became so problematic for three reasons. Firstly, fundholders usually cannot act as ruthless purchasers. Not only is there a contradiction between the doctor acting in the patient's interest and the rationing of resources within a limited fund, but local providers (hospitals and community services) may not always be influenced by fundholders' interests, and choice of provider may be limited or non-existent (Freudenstein, 1993).

Secondly, fundholders are as much a threat as an opportunity for local health planning. Fundholders' decisions about placing resources are primarily budget-led because the pressure to avoid overspending is so great. Overspent fundholders would simply lack the money to adhere to wider health policies, even if they wanted to.

Finally, no school of general practice sees itself as simply having a gatekeeper function that controls access to specialist medicine, but fundholding as currently pursued stresses the role of the prudent gatekeeper. The costs of specialist care may be reduced by better chronic disease management in the community, and through primary and secondary prevention in general practice, but we cannot be certain about that and the opposite may be true. Inadequate screening, health maintenance and disease management by cost-conscious general practitioners may create more problems for specialists, requiring more money, not less, to solve them. A mechanism that encourages reduced referral or prescribing on the assumption that other forms of treatment will then develop to make this reduction possible is running far ahead of the evidence.

This situation came about because fundholding developed as an ideological construct, rather than a scientific hypothesis. Fundholding is an idea that evolved from a micro-economic model of general practice development (Bosanquet & Leese, 1989) and has been promoted by 'ignorant experts' (Alan Maynard, unpublished discussion paper) but never tested in pilot studies, despite authoritative advice that this should be done (Smith,

1989). Designed as a political solution to 'kick start' the NHS internal market, fundholding has become an end, rather than a means to an end (Willis, 1992). The micro-economic model described by Bosanquet suggests that the main motor for development of general practice is a combination of rising populations, available space and people willing to work as support workers for low salaries. This model seems to explain the expansion of shire county practices in the 1970s and 1980s, and to account for the relative stagnation of general practice in the cities, where these conditions did not apply and where professional leadership acted as an alternative catalyst.

This promotion of an untested economic mechanism meets the needs of some general practitioners, for a number of reasons. It offers a new and much more patient centered approach to organising medical care, it addresses the long-standing rivalry in British medicine between generalists and specialists (Honigsbaum, 1979), and it provides a new career path in a profession that has few escape routes for the professional who is weary of life on the medical treadmill.

The old joke that the NHS would be a great institution if it weren't for the patients reveals the organisation's priorities. Hospitals in the National Health Service have functioned on an assembly line basis, with patients apportioned to different tracks to be processed in different specialist departments, then shuffling along in the queue for out-patient care or speeding along through in-patient wards. The features of the assembly line were taken for granted. The investigation and treatment of illnesses was broken down into component tasks, often performed by separate professions, and often by relatively unskilled workers in each professional group. The line usually worked slowly and in a sequence that met the needs of the assembly workers rather than their patients, so that consultation was followed by X-rays and tests, then by further consultations about results, then by treatment and finally by review, sometimes interminably and often without clear purpose. The exit for one assembly line might be the loading ramp for the next, not because the patient needed this order of organisation but because it existed. As medicine became increasingly specialised the number and variety of assembly lines increased and hospital care became fragmented in a Fordist nightmare of industrial production in which staff struggled to maintain the individuality of their patients, and in which cynicism and burn-out became normal.

The fundholding idea offered an alternative way of working, since it gave the initiative in the organisation of medical care for individuals to general practitioners, not specialists. General practice had evolved with a strong sense of its holism, of the ability of general practitioners to see the social and psychological sides of medicine as well as the organic aspect, and in rhetoric the patient was centre stage. The reality was different, of course, but the prospect of being able to customise medical care to individuals simply by buying it and forcing once-inflexible specialists to alter their ways of working through use of contracts appealed to the ideology of the wise, concerned and knowledgeable GP, as well as chiming with the consumerist culture of Thatcher's Britain. Fundholders do not, in the main, do much of this post-Fordist type of assembly work, pulling together different components for individual patients, because block contracts with and bulk buying from limited local providers are more cost-effective in time, but the idea remains a powerful one.[2]

Fundholding also promises to invert the power relationship between the superior hospital specialist and the inferior general practitioner. General practitioners, who have tolerated poor relative status for a generation or two, can now try to control the behaviour of hospital specialists who have behaved arrogantly and ignorantly towards their peers in the community for a long time, as well as taking the great bulk of NHS resources. In so inverting the power relationship, fundholding reinforces the notion of omniscience that lies beneath the surface of generalism - the idea that generalists are jacks of all trades who can do anything, including determine the pattern of specialist medical care.

General practice is an onerous job. The daily encounter with distress, illness and pain takes its toll on practitioners, especially if they throw themselves into their work with enthusiasm and commitment. Ways of alleviating the emotional and intellectual exhaustion of those who work on the treadmill are relatively few, and promotion away from the coalface to a management position, which is the usual experience of hospital professionals, is denied most general practitioners. Fundholding has offered a solution to this. Doctors who are not attracted to the politics of the local GP power structure, nor to the tasks of postgraduate training, nor to academic practice and university posts, can now through fundholding express their entrepreneurial skills and occupy themselves with an important and rewarding function that diverts from the daily grind of seeing the sick and the sad.

MODERNISATION - THE REALITY

Nevertheless, fundholding as presently conceived and practiced is unlikely to survive, even if a future government wants it to. The underlying trends in general practice are working against general practitioners taking a central, decisive role in the leadership of a primary care based and market driven health service. The development of general practice in the 1970s and, especially, the 1980s is as likely to down-grade the political role of the general practitioner as to elevate it, and understanding the modernisation process within general practice is essential in understanding future options for the NHS.

The 1980s was the decade of modernisation in general practice. During the late 1970s and early 1980s general practice became a more attractive career option for doctors as hospital medicine became more bureaucratic and cash-limited, and the working conditions of junior hospital doctors deteriorated becoming the subject of widespread criticism. The number of doctors entering the GP career path increased steadily throughout the 1980s, so that the workforce grew from 28,000 in 1983 to 30,500 in 1988.

This recruitment to general practice produced a younger workforce with more women doctors than ever before. Considerable increases in the numbers of general practitioners occurred in every age band up to 44, with women doctors constituting nearly a third of those under 35, compared with 9 per cent of those aged 65 or over (Pereira Gray, 1992). This increase in the proportion of women entering general practice has had a significant impact on the politics of the profession. New entrants to general practice act as levers for change in organisations suffering inertia and sometimes stagnation, introducing new ideas and new work methods that help modernise the organisations. When this innovator group includes large numbers of women who are also concerned about their own young families, the agenda for change is feminised, with a particular emphasis on limiting working hours to realistic levels. As we shall see, this ambition conflicts with both the tradition of 24 hour availability and the increasing range of activities that need to be compressed into the normal working day.

In one sense the workload of general practitioners appears to have fallen. As the number of GPs increased, the average list size fell to below 2000, compared with 2413 in 1970. The reduction in list sizes permitted an increase in average consultation time from seven to nine minutes during the 1980s. By 1990 the proportion of consultations lasting 10 minutes or more had increased to a quarter, compared with under a fifth in 1986. Dedicated clinics for ante-natal care, child health surveillance and the management of chronic diseases became established in general practice during the 1980s, and their consultation times were nearer 12 minutes by the end of the decade.

The number of consultations per patient per year appeared to increase slightly during the middle of the eighties, but the average figures conceal major changes in specific age groups. For example, the proportion of children under five seeing a general practitioner in a given time period had doubled in ten years, to eight consultations per year in 1987. Likewise, there had been a shift in the provision of family planning services to young women, with a 25 per cent increase in numbers between 1978 and 1987 and a concomitant reduction in attendance at family planning clinics provided by community health services, so that by 1987 about 70 per cent of contraceptive care was being provided in general practice (Pereira Gray, 1992).

As more time was given to individual patients, more time was also demanded by other aspects of practice activity. By

1990, an average general practitioner was working 65 hours a week (not counting medico-political activity and continuing professional education), just under 24 of these being 'on call' - that is, available for out-of-hours contact with patients. This represented a 7 per cent increase in the clinical working week, but a 3 per cent reduction in on-call time, compared with the middle of the decade.

Factors affecting workload in the 1980s included :

◆ the sex of the doctor (male general practitioners working longer hours than their female colleagues)

◆ the availability of equipment like computers, glucometers and peak flow meters

◆ access to physiotherapy

◆ and organisation in a group (GMP workload survey 1989-90, DoH).

In short, modernisation of general practice, in both organisational and clinical senses, led to higher workloads for general practitioners. However, not all of this increase in workload towards the end of the eighties was attributable to changes in clinical activity and the content of the lengthened consultation. Figure 1 shows the changes in hours allocated to different aspects of general practice work between the middle and the end of the decade.

FIGURE 1   Changes in time devoted to different components of GP work, 1985-6 to 1989-90

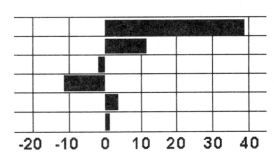

It appears that general practitioners compensated for a very significant increase in practice administration by reducing time devoted to home visiting and teaching. The number of GP home visits remained unchanged despite falling list sizes suggesting that home visits became briefer.

One casualty in this reorganisation of working time and priorities was maternity care. In the early 1980s, 25 per cent of GPs were involved in intra-partum care (Marsh, 1985). Now the proportion is less than 10 per cent and falling (Bull, 1988) and some question whether there is a future for general practice obstetrics at all (Jewell & Smith, 1990). The espousal by the Major government of an openly consumerist approach to maternity care with the publication of 'Changing Childbirth' is now pushing midwives to centre stage in supporting women in pregnancy and labour, with a further reduction in the contribution of general practitioners.

The number of consultations per patient per year appeared to increase slightly during the middle of the decade, but by the end of the 1980s there was a significant reduction in the numbers of general medical consultations, and only the numbers seen in dedicated clinics (for asthma, diabetes, hypertension and other chronic conditions, or for maternity care and child health) remained unchanged (GMP survey). In 1990 an average general practitioner would have 118 surgery consultations and 22 home visits, compared with 124 consultations and 26 home visits five years earlier.

THE SHIFT AWAY FROM ACUTE CARE

It appears that the trend first documented in the 1970s for general practitioners to have fewer patient contacts per episode of illness had continued, and that re-orientation of clinical work towards chronic disease management and preventive care might have reduced general practitioners' daytime availability for the management of acute illnesses. Two pieces of evidence point towards this conclusion: the increase in out-of-hours activity in accident and emergency departments; and the increase in night calls in general practice.

Use of accident and emergency departments had doubled between 1961 and 1983, and continued to rise throughout the 1980s (Milner *et al*, 1988; Social Trends, 1993). There was also evidence that A&E departments were providing up to 47 per cent of first patient contacts in some (urban) areas (Williams *et al*, 1985). Hospital specialists can now claim that accident and emergency departments are part of the mosaic of primary care, and there are moves to recruit general practitioners to work in A&E departments where they can help with the minor end of the department's workload whilst being frugal in arranging tests and investigations, and in involving specialist services. General practitioners no longer operate as gatekeepers for large periods of time at night and over weekends, and therefore hospitals now have significant primary care 'first contact' functions.

Night calls in general practice also appeared to increase during the 1980s, with a rate of 10 per 1000 registered patients in 1976, and between 15.5 (albeit in one district) in 1981. Large variations occurred in the rate of night visits, with different small scale studies in the 1980s showing from 14 to 35 night calls per 1000 patients per year (Hallam, 1994). These calls are clinically similar to the daytime workload of general practitioners, and can only be interpreted as 'urgent medical problems' by categorising anxiety about health as a feature of urgency. The availability of the service may be a factor promoting its use, with the reduced availability of general practitioners acting synergistically to promote the growth of accident and emergency departments.

Some of the increase in night calls may also reflect demographic change rather than changes in the provision of general practitioner care. The proportion of households with a telephone increased from 75 per cent in 1981 to nearly 90 per cent in 1990, while social support of groups with high levels of morbidity may have decreased. Elderly people living alone increased from 22 per cent of households in 1981 to 26 per cent in 1991, whilst single parents with small children increased from 2 per cent to 4 per cent of households in the same time (Williams, 1993).

One of the responses that general practitioners had made

to the extension of their working week and the intensification of clinical activity was to reduce their on-call commitment, either by sharing it with a larger pool of local colleagues, or by sub-contracting it to commercial deputising agencies, or both. Between the middle and the end of the 1980s the proportion of the working week spent on-call had fallen from 32.4 per cent to 29.7 per cent, while the percentage of patient contacts made by commercial deputising services had increased from 8.7 per cent to 11 per cent (GMP Workload Survey). Two thirds of general practitioners used practice rotas for all or some on-call periods, and up to 30 per cent collaborated with neighbouring practices for some on-call duties (Hallam, 1994) By 1989 46 per cent of night calls were made by deputising services (*General Practice in the NHS: a new contract*, HMSO, London 1989) and nearly one third of general practitioners reported no personal, regular commitment to their practice's night cover (Hallam, 1994) Some of the deputising services were organised as doctors co-operatives, but the majority remain commercial organisations, mostly situated in cities or large towns where, typically, 70-80 per cent of GP's made use of them. Co-operatives are growing in number as the limitations of commercial organisations, including the brief contacts made by doctors paid on a piece-work basis and the perverse incentive of for-profit organisations to increase demand rather than contain it, are realised.

THE DECLINE OF THE GATEKEEPER FUNCTION

The slow withdrawal of general practitioners from acute care for which as a whole they are well enough trained, and their re-orientation to chronic disease management (for which the profession is as a whole poorly trained and ill-organised) has eroded the gatekeeper function of primary care, with obvious financial implications for the Department of Health. It is hardly surprising that referrals from general practitioners to specialists should become a controversial topic, since the boundaries of general practitioners' responsibilities seem to have been widening as the scope of specialist medicine itself enlarged. By the end of the 1980s there were nearly 40 million out-patient appointments made in NHS hospitals each year, between 60 and 80 per cent of them originating from general practice, depending on specialty (Coulter, Noone, Goldacre, 1989). Referral from general practice to specialist care became dysfunctional and to some extent incongruent with patient expectation during the 1980s. Default rates averaging 20 per cent and reaching 40 per cent for ENT referrals were noted in one study (McGlade, *et al*, 1988), whilst another showed that a quarter of patients attending a medical outpatient clinic in one city also had appointments with other clinics for the same problem (JRCP, 25, 1991, pp33-5), each suggesting that there was scope for greater efficiency in providing specialist outpatient services. Referral appeared to be linked to the availability of specialists, not to local need (Roland & Morris, 1988).

FUTURE DEVELOPMENTS

Proposals for the development of general practice originating from the progressive wing of the medical profession implicitly accepted the new paradigm of medical care and emphasized the new orientation to chronic disease management without discussing the implications of abdicating responsibility for acute care. For example, the GP could function as a medical officer of health for their own practice population (Mant & Anderson, 1985; Hart, 1984). This function might include:

(i)   Monitoring the state of health of the practice population and producing an annual report comparing local with regional and national health statistics

(ii) Surveillance of local environmental hazards and infectious diseases

(iii) Planning of care, including maintaining chronic disease and disability registers

(iv) Auditing the effectiveness of preventive programmes

(v) Evaluating the effect of medical intervention on the population - perhaps through a network of research practices.

Such a job description is a long way from the 'family doctor' role model that most people (and probably most general practitioners) understand, and begs the question, if general practitioners are to be busy with monitoring, surveying, planning, auditing and evaluating who will see the people who get ill?

Increasingly, this task will fall to hospitals (for those who cannot afford private medicine) which will respond to the demand for medical attention by further extension of A&E departments, enlargement and dispersal of out-patient clinics, and the development of 'hospital outreach' that will take specialist services to people in their localities, alongside or independently of general practitioners. The more that general practitioners attempt or are pressured into becoming the determinants of local health service policy and the controllers of local funding, the more that hospitals will struggle to survive in the new market by pulling patients towards themselves, so that the power of public demand overrides the intentions of purchasers to switch resources from one provider to another. To be a main provider of acute care is, in such a situation, to occupy a pole position, for, by definition, acute care leads contracts rather than waiting on them.

The incoming government at the end of the 1990s has many difficult questions to answer. Can a 'primary care-led NHS' emerge, given the real underlying trends in general practice? Is there a big enough cadre of entrepreneurial doctors who can kick start the internal market, or will the market be stabilised by powerful institutional forces that easily overcome a generation of general practitioners who are not really contenders in the struggle for power? Would fundholding, if successful, undermine equity in the provision of medical care so much that it would open a political sore that no amount of delegation from the Department of Health to outlying quangos could heal? And are there alternatives to fundholding, the internal market in the NHS and the franchising of medicine that would retain the gains made in the last five years, or is the only option to turn the clock back?

NOTES

1. Low pay for most NHS staff, limited replacement of old buildings, undermanagement, price controls on pharmaceuticals and developing general practice as a public sector franchise (see page 76) have all contributed to the low cost of the NHS.

2. As it does in social work, where the case manager would be able to buy flexible services to meet the needs of individual clients...if the services existed, if there was more money available, and if there were not so many clients.

References

Bosanquet N. & Leese B., *Family doctors and economic incentives*, Dartmouth, Aldershot 1989.

Bradlow J. & Coulter A., 'Effect of fundholding and indicative prescribing schemes on general practitioners' prescribing costs', *BMJ*, 307, 1993, pp1186-9.

Bull M. J. V., 'General practice obstetrics ... is there a future?' *Update*, 37, 1988 p590.

Central Statistical Office, *Social Trends*, HMSO, London 1993.

Coulter A., Noone A., Goldacre M., 'General Practitioners referrals to specialist outpatient clinics. 1. Why general practitioners refer patients to specialist outpatient clinics', *BMJ*, 299, 1989, pp304-306.

Department of Health, Cmnd 9771, *Primary Health Care - An agenda for Discussion*, HMSO, London 1986.

Doctors' and Dentists' Review Body, General Medical Practitioners workload survey 1989-90, Department of Health, London 1991.

Freudenstein U., 'Fundholding from the inside', *Medical World*, 13, 1993, pp10-11.

Glennerster H, Owens P. & Matsaganis M., 'A foothold for fundholding', Kings Fund Institute, London 1992.

Hallam L., 'Primary medical care outside normal working hours: review of published work', *BMJ*, 308, 1994, pp249-53.

Hart J. T., 'Community General Practitioners', *BMJ*, 288, 1984, pp1670-3.

Honigsbaum F., 'The Division in British Medicine', Kogan Page, London 1979.

Houghton K., 'Peak practices', *Health Service Journal*, 103, 1993, pp26-7.

Jewell D. & Smith L. 'Is there a future for general practitioner obstetrics?' *RCGP Members Reference Book*, Royal College of General Practitioners, London 1990, p239.

Leese B. & Smedley E., 'Costing GP budgets', *Health Service Journal*, 96, 1989, p1310.

Mant D. & Anderson P., 'Community General Practitioner', *Lancet*, ii, 1985, pp1114-7.

Marsh G. N.' 'General practice participation in the Northern Region in 1983', *BMJ*, 290, 1985 p973.

Maxwell M., Heaney D., Howie J. G. R. & Noble S., 'General practice fundholding: observations on prescribing patterns and costs using the defined daily dose method', *BMJ*, 307, 1993, pp1190-4.

McGlade K. J., Bradley T., Murphy G. J. & Lundy G. P. P., 'Referrals to hospitals by general practutioners: a study of compliance and communication', *BMJ*, 297, 1988, pp1246-8.

Milner P. C., Nichol J. P. & Williams B. T., 'Variation in demand for accident and emergency departments in England, 1974-1985', *Journal of Epidemiology and Community Health*, 42, 1988, pp274-8.

Pereira Gray D., 'Facts and figures about general practice', *RCGP Members reference book*, Royal College of General Practitioners, London 1991.

Roland M. O. & Morris R., 'Are referrals by general practitioners influenced by the availability of consultants?' *BMJ*, 297, 1988, pp699-700.

Smith R., 'Words from the source: an interview with Alain Enthoven', *BMJ*, 298, 1989, pp1166-8.

Somanta A., Haider Y. & Roffe C., 'An audit of patients attending a general medical follow-up clinic', *Journal of the Royal College of Physicians*, 25, 1991, pp33-5.

Stanworth J. & Smith B., *Franchising for the Small Business*, Blackwell, Oxford 1991.

Teeling-Smith G., 'The economics of prescribing and underprescribing', in Wells F. O. (ed), *Medicines: responsible prescribing*, Queens University, Belfast 1992.

Williams B. T., Dixon R. A. & Nicholl J. P., 'Provision of first contact care out-of-hours in four urban areas in England', *BMJ*, 291, 1985, pp1689-92.

Williams B. T., 'Night visits in general practice', *BMJ*, 306, 1993, pp734-5.

Willis A., 'Who needs fundholding?' *Health Service Journal*, 30 April 1992, pp24-25.

PUBLIC HEALTH, HEALTH PROMOTION AND BROADER HEALTH STRATEGY

Alison McCallum

In Britain the health departments have never had a clear public health responsibility. The Chief Medical Officer's annual report provides a selective analysis of public health problems, but there has never been any sense that recommendations are prioritised and translated into action plans for progress towards improved health at local and national level. In recent years, the co-ordination of health promotion at national level has been the role of the Health Education Authority (HEA). But while the HEA has concentrated on high profile, single issue campaigns (HEA, 1995), attempts to foster community-based strategies for health improvement have been lost. Community-based health promotion has developed nationally through the community health movement but in many areas links with health service decision makers have never been formed.

In this mixed environment, there have been several attempts to implement high profile strategies for health improvement, including *Health for All* (WHO, 1993), its offspring *Healthy Cities* (Ashton J. (ed), 1992), strategies designed tackle inequalities in health, and the current health strategy for England, *Health of the Nation* (Department of Health, 1992).

Health for All

Health for All (HFA) was established to promote international support for a common agenda for health improvement (Rathwell, 1992). The underlying principles of HFA are well known: equity, health promotion, community participation, multi-sectoral collaboration, and primary health care. To measure progress, indicators of avoidable or premature morbidity and mortality were defined as targets and many governments, including Britain's, agreed to support action to achieve them.

The commitment and political will to implement programmes designed to meet HFA objectives has been patchy (Sutton, 1994). Nationally, the long term commitment to social and economic reform required to supplement and support behavioural change has been ignored. Since the 1980s, the WHO decade of safe water and sanitation, water privatisation and public sector funding policies in Britain have reduced access to clean water for people on low incomes, while the Criminal Justice Act may reduce the duty of care to travellers. Where information is not sought on the health needs of particular groups, their needs may remain unexpressed and neither prevention or treatment programmes will be designed to address them. HFA has been a landmark in the translation of policy commitment into public relations.

Healthy Cities

The Healthy Cities movement grew out of the HFA implementation programme. City networking was seen as one way to move health up the social and political agenda, undertaking research and evaluation (Ashton, 1992), achieving grassroots commitment to community participation, challenging inequalities in health and improving intersectoral collaboration (Miller Jones, Simpson, Wilson, 1991).

Healthy Cities was based on the nineteenth-century Health of Towns initiative, formed to press for legislative changes that would improve the public health (Ashton, 1992). The initiative, which had its first success within four years, was based on information sharing, detailed analysis of routine data and direct communication with the public. But Healthy Cities has not met with the same unqualified success. Uptake across Britain has been uneven, and projects include a varied mix of grassroots work and top level public relations. Of course, this does not necessarily imply failure. The strategy may be to inspire communities by example while communicating with decision makers on their own terms. Some projects, in which local communities have helped to design urban regeneration programmes to tackle inequalities and reduce avoidable morbidity (Duncan, 1990), illustrate a future for joint working between health promotion, public health and commissioning authorities, despite the mixed economy in health.

Changing the wider environment in politics and health, however, is not simply a challenge that awaits application of the appropriate methodology or method of dissemination. In some areas, dialogue between agencies has been inconsistent and the work required to sustain change has been neglected or thwarted following hostile take-overs by the organisations and systems that the Healthy Cities network was established to challenge. Overall, Healthy Cities has been more successful in achieving change at local level than as a national or international health public health movement.

Improving health by tackling inequalities

Although *absolute* levels of income in a country are an important measure of basic living standards, and hence health, recent public health efforts in developed countries have concentrated on the relationship between relative social and material deprivation and ill-health. *The Black Report* illuminated and publicised this relationship in England but, despite its clear purpose, strong arguments and convincing authors, little positive government action resulted (DHSS, 1980; Phillimore, Beattie and Townsend, 1994). In contrast, the Netherlands has encouraged and funded a national programme of research in this area with strong cross-party support (Mackenbach, 1994). Socio-economic inequalities in health occur in all countries although the magnitude of the differences varies (Kunst, 1994). Across developed countries, the difference in life expectancy between the richest and poorest fifths of the population is 6.3 years; the difference in disability-free life expectancy is greater, at 14.3 years (Robine, Ritchie, 1991). The gap is narrowest in Norway, an oil-rich country with comprehensive social programmes and limited variation in health-related behaviours such as smoking.

Although the methods used to measure inequalities in health in the 1990s are considered better developed than those used previously, many such 'new' techniques have been convincing academic audiences for approximately a decade both that concerted action to reduce inequality is necessary and that its effects are measurable (Abelin *et al*, 1987). Ministers who abdicate responsibility for inaction by feigned interest in residual confounding are wholly unconvincing.

This decade of disinterest has illustrated that expert opinion and factual evidence alone cannot stimulate the political will necessary to undertake the complex and sustained programme of change required. Abolishing child poverty, for example, requires strategic and operational change: new health and social care initiatives, political change through government action on child benefit, maternity allowances and structural change. Mobilising public support is hampered by the difficulty in presenting the 'big picture'.

The public health commitment to tackling inequalities, however, is also an ethical one. Klein argues that attention to the role of education and housing in health confuses strategies for health improvement with social engineering (Klein, 1993). To neglect these areas, however, is also social engineering. All societies are stratified and even in publicly funded systems access to health care follows this stratification (Field, 1989), either through the purchase of private care or through more assertive use of the system. Equal access for equal need will not produce for the poor the same improvements in health that will be achieved by the rich. Activity to improve health must emphasise greater attention to those with most to gain.

The role of public health medicine in tackling inequalities in health is clear. First, to examine the population attributable risk of socio-economic differences in smoking, obesity, living and working conditions, levels of psychosocial stress and social support, and access to timely and effective health care. Second, to plan and implement effective strategies to reduce these risks (Mackenbach 1992). Measuring the improvement expected requires increasingly sophisticated methods of evaluation, able to cope with multiple outcomes. Such methods are not yet routinely available, highlighting gaps in current public health measurement as well as action (Hennesy *et al*, 1994; Sacco, 1995).

Perhaps if *The Black Report*, *Health for All* and *Healthy Cities* had used the language of the market, more would have been achieved. None have been explicit about the level of either costs or benefits of the proposed programmes. Explicit recommendations that tackled costs and demand containment, while addressing variations in health status and social deprivation, might have led health ministers and chief executives to act.

This ambivalent relationship between the state and those involved in developing and implementing health strategies, combined with the failure of either to be explicit about the level of support for particular objectives and the effectiveness of the methods used to achieve them, has left health promotion priorities confused and individual professionals often powerless (Stevenson and Burke, 1992).

Health of the Nation

The potential to achieve HFA principles remains in Britain, because national health strategies have developed to link prevention and treatment (Dekker, 1994). *Health of the Nation* is the English health strategy, and similar strategies exist for the other countries of the UK. In theory, the principles upon which policy decisions are made, for example equity, should become explicit. Similarly, responsibility for monitoring implementation of policy using, for example, quantifiable health targets, can now be agreed.

In England, five target areas were chosen: accidents, cancer, cardiovascular disease, mental health, and HIV and sexual health. Clearly, these are important causes of premature and avoidable mortality and morbidity. They also offer opportunities for all parts of the health service to work together, and to collaborate with local authorities and other agencies. The areas to be tackled by *Health of the Nation* were limited, however, to those for which targets could be set and progress monitored using current and planned routine data sources. The opportunity to improve health intelligence through the broader application of initiatives including, for example, the Oxford record linkage project (Gill, 1993), the community health information systems project (Suffolk

Health Authority, 1994) and primary care based needs assessment, have been ignored. Again, recognition of excellence in both theoretical and practical application of epidemiological modelling, surveillance (Declich, 1994) and monitoring has been absent and the opportunity for clear public health leadership squandered.

The implementation process, too, has been narrow, and effective avenues for change have been ignored. Attempts to reduce the ill-health due to cardiovascular disease and cancer have been hampered by the lack of central action on, for example, tobacco advertising. Despite the special relationship with the US, Britain has ignored America's few successful health initiatives. The development of *Health of the Nation* offered an opportunity, not only to ban tobacco advertising, but also to establish an equivalent to the Fair Political Practices Commission with enabling legislation on freedom of information for health purposes. Such a body could, as in the US, monitor the costs of anti-health propaganda: advertising, political lobbying, and funding of legal cases (Begay, Traynor, Glantz, 1993). This would have enabled a more balanced review of opportunities for, and threats to, improved health in the development of national and local health strategies, formally linking health protection with measurement of health improvement.

But *Health of the Nation* is a top down agenda. The tactics used to engage those committed to improving health, particularly in public health and health promotion, must be disentangled from the other agenda that *Health of the Nation* helps to implement. The target setting and monitoring components are part of a process of gaining professional assent to greater managerial control (Ben Shlomo, 1991), with performance assessed only against pre-specified criteria which are limited in number, nature and scope.

It is important, however, that while we are not naive about the mixed agendas of *Health of the Nation*, we grasp the opportunities it offers. We must recognise why the original strategy had nothing specific to say about equity (Dekker, 1994); why there is no commitment to tackle structural issues and why targets require reductions in mortality before morbidity. The recent publication of *Variations in Health* (Department of Health, 1995) may simply reflect a desire to minimise the shortcomings of *Health of the Nation* before the next election.

Many of the health strategies discussed above, target large groups; it is difficult to design and implement programmes at city level. A more effective strategy might be to increase the proportion of neighbourhood development projects that are linked formally to other projects with similar objectives.

Health promotion in primary care

The current programme of health promotion in primary care, which provides financial incentives to encourage ineffective and inappropriate initiatives, illustrates preventive efforts at their most unconvincing (Toon, 1995). Primary care in Britain is designed to identify those who are already ill, to target early intervention towards those at increased risk of specific conditions, and to ensure that both groups remain as healthy as possible. Practice initiatives to detect common abnormalities or prevent illness should complement population based approaches; the method chosen should depend on the balance between likely benefits and costs at individual and population level.

Public health specialists can help to assess and prioritise the needs of the practice population, identifying which activities are best tackled in the surgery, for example anti-hypertensive care, and when to use the practice list as a small area population, for example to improve access to free or low cost leisure facilities for those with established cardiovascular disease (Faculty Strategies for Health Promotion in Primary Care 1993). If *Health for All* or *Health of the Nation* is to be implemented successfully, both prevention and general medical services must remain free at the point of use while a partnership between public health, health promotion and primary care develops to deliver the information, skills and support required (Green, 1995).

The limited success to date of *Health for All, Healthy Cities*, and *Health of the Nation*, and attempts to tackle inequalities in health suggest that a much stronger and more assertive leadership is required from the professions. Current conflicts, for public health and health promotion in particular, are over priorities other than those central to their own performance objectives. It is no longer possible for professional judgement to determine the appropriate balance between influence in the health service and broader public health action.

CURRENT INFLUENCES ON PUBLIC HEALTH STRATEGY

The NHS Reforms
The unpiloted and unevaluated health care reforms that have been introduced in Britain since 1989, are a prime example of ideologically-driven change. Such reform, without commitment to reflection and evaluation, may simply result in an organisational framework which makes the implementation of public health, health promotion and health services research programmes impossible.

There is a risk, in a 'consumer-led' system, that the power of individual demand will override considerations of community benefit, reducing commissioning of care to the sum of individual patient transactions. If personal needs take precedence over those of the population then not only will the public health perspective have been marginalised but the opportunity to improve overall health status will have been severely restricted. Demand must be only one of many factors considered when assessing whether an intervention should be purchased or provided (Stevens, 1995).

Monitoring data similar to that required for *Health for All* (Dekker, 1994) could enable review of population-based health status data, the extent to which the appropriateness, efficiency and effectiveness of intervention is considered in the development of health policy, the emphasis given to health promotion, specific disease prevention, and the role of government and other agencies.

Rationing
Rationing has been embraced by some public health doctors. This acceptance may be used by the government to legitimise

the view that some groups are more worthy of treatment than others, while those with money or influence buy private care or manage the information process to alter rationing decisions. The only defence against this is to insist that the values underlying rationing decisions are explicit and to develop a sophisticated understanding of the effectiveness of both intervention and non-intervention, neither discriminating against nor encouraging the introduction of new technology without formal assessment (Stevens, Colin-Jones, Gabbay, 1995).

It is important to assess the effects of non-intervention as well as of the latest new technology. The literature on effectiveness, cost effectiveness and cost utility measures such as QALYs emphasises acute over chronic disease, rehabilitation and health maintenance, yet most acute care is provided in the context of an underlying chronic disease process. To examine acute care without regard to the longer term requirements for care will distort the allocation of finance, personnel and expertise between sectors and specialties caring for the same patients (Van den Bos, 1991). At its most absurd, resources devoted towards amputations in diabetic patients might increase, while access to services which could prevent vascular disease might be reduced. The failure to apply robust techniques to the evaluation of prevention and care as well as cure has artificially limited the debate on priority setting to services that are easily measured and costed.

Some warn that doctors should not be involved in decisions about rationing care for individuals. However, if public health specialists are not involved, some decisions will be made solely on the NHS costs of an episode of care. Public health specialists must assess and present formal risk assessments of health care choices in a way that enables the appropriate combination of patients, professionals and society to take such decisions. A more constructive response would be, wherever possible, that doctors should not support disinvestment on the basis of costs alone but should ensure that care can be provided according to clinical criteria reflecting both ability to benefit (Bayley, 1995) and the consequences of non-intervention.

Without these safeguards there will be the impression that rationing 'less effective' treatment is merely a cost cutting activity.

A key role for public health medicine within the NHS, therefore, is to campaign for the achievement of health potential through effective health care interventions. Ability to benefit should be the only basis on which access to intervention is limited, with all citizens entitled to an agreed level of palliative care.

Implementing public health action

The reforms have not only affected public health strategy and values, but specific tasks have become more difficult as a result of 'commercial secrecy'. Between the start of the reforms and the emergence of official guidance confirming the public health medicine role (HC, 1992, p123), some consultants in communicable disease control had their involvement in infection control in trusts limited, despite the potential risks to the wider population.

It has also been difficult to access the public health skills of trust staff. Health visitors, for example, receive a basic training in epidemiology and neighbourhood needs assessment. Contracts, however, are returning them to work of unproven value, such as unprioritised visiting of mothers and children under five, rather than developing their potential to design and deliver needs-led programmes. If the reforms were introduced to release resources by reducing embedded inefficiencies in health care delivery, why replace professionally driven inefficiency with new structural inefficiencies?

The public health perspective emphasises an *overall* assessment of medical and social benefit to maximise the benefit of interventions for health. The potential conflict between public health and market approaches may be illustrated in relation to exercise (Sallis, Mackenzie, 1991). The public health view supports initiatives like *Sport for All*, which aimed to reduce inequality of access to sport and leisure facilities, developing enjoyment and lifelong participation in physical activity. In contrast, the competitive team sport ethos of the market emphasises the identification of a winning elite at the expense of the many (Moore, 1994). The collaborative philosophy illustrated by *Sport for All* sits uncomfortably with a competition-focused health service: effective public health programmes require co-operation between agencies which are now expected to compete to maintain their share of resources.

Where do PHM and HP belong?

The conflict between independence and influence highlighted by the Abrams report (NHS Management Executive, 1993) is part of a broader debate about the relative importance of the public health agenda versus its location within the health and social care bureaucracy. The public health perspective has suffered from its location within a bureaucratic structure that uses existing provision to plan for the future rather than planning to achieve improvements in health.

In 1974, the medical officers of health employed by local authorities were brought into the NHS as specialists in community medicine, now public health medicine. The NHS reforms have now cast public health doctors in a potentially adversarial role, aligning them against clinicians in a politicised bureaucracy. They have been the bearers of bad news about limited resources and have been reluctant collaborators in the implementation of unpopular reforms. This position contrasts with the specialty's view of itself as advocacy based, ensuring that a broad view of health is advanced, and promoting the idea of evidence-based services (Quam, 1989; Mackenbach, 1995).

The formal inclusion of public health as a corporate function has both advantages and disadvantages. To reduce premature and avoidable morbidity and mortality within any health care structure, public health must have influence at all levels; but some current corporate priorities may be difficult to share (Scambler, Goraya, 1994). Independent public health agencies would solve some of the corporate dilemma but without a voice at the executive table the impact of proposals for public health action is likely to be limited (Flynn, 1992). While much public health work and benefit lies outside the NHS, there must be a balance to be struck between independence from and influence over the health care services.

Health promotion faces similar conflicts about the relative importance of agenda and location. Since health promotion is a tool that enables individuals and communities to improve control over the factors affecting their health, health promoting activities must be found on both sides of the purchaser-provider divide. The role of health promotion in guiding strategy and commissioning activity is clearly a public health function, and to avoid investing in ineffective and inappropriate health promotion activities, health authorities require expert and impartial advice. Health promotion departments responsible to one trust board, however, can find their ability to work with other agencies, including rival trusts, compromised. Contract income from health promotion may be insufficient to justify external activities that detract from the rest of the host trust's 'core business'.

Health promotion views itself as a focus for empowerment but, depending on the political climate, it may be coerced, through central direction or through organisational positioning and limited resources, into acting as an agent for social control (Grace, 1995). This will occur when individual lifestyle factors are emphasised beyond their ability to produce health benefits, or when health becomes a commodity with individuals and populations as consumers.

Priorities for public health practice, organisation and action

A narrow interpretation of the Abrams' report could pose a significant threat to the public health objectives of health commissions, restricting the public health role to advice on commissioning priorities and preoccupying directors of public health with corporate activity. If unchecked, such tendencies could reduce the profile of directors of public health as an independent advocates for the population.

Current priorities for public health medicine must be interpreted in the light of these threats. Public health medicine should lead commissioning for change but should not take over contracting. The annual and cyclical nature of purchasing with its recurrent operational problems and demands for short term solutions sits uneasily with the longer term public health view of contracting as one mechanism for achieving incremental improvements in health (Stevens, Colin-Jones, 1995). If public health medicine becomes involved in the minutiae of contract reviews and corporate responsibilities, the broader public health role will be neglected.

While the technical and theoretical aspects of public health work can be undertaken at national and international level, their interpretation and application are the responsibility of public health doctors at local level. The annual public health report, which is independent of the employing authority, should demonstrate a formal link between description of health problems and action for improvement. This requires that public health drives local health strategy to ensure that no section of the population is forgotten, and that the potential for effective intervention in rare, unfashionable, or under-researched conditions is formally reviewed.

Although public health medicine has a responsibility to develop and support a population focus across a range of issues, much can be done in conjunction with other disciplines. Public health must maintain and strengthen its external links, rekindling its relationship with local government action on social and environmental factors that affect health (ALG, 1995).

Public health and local government

Public health specialists had their original home in local government, but today their relationships with local authorities are, by and large, tenuous. Centralisation of power, conflicts over policy and implementation, and changing relationships between members and officers in local and national government, have conspired to make collaboration difficult, even where objectives are shared. Conflict within the public health medicine establishment over the priority which should be given to communicable disease and environmental health has limited partnership in this area (Campbell, 1994). Public health doctors are wary of the limitations on environmental health officers' powers. As local authority employees, individual EHOs are unable to comment freely on local authority action, requiring them to use their professional body at national level to lobby for changes in legislation and practice. This contrasts with the requirement for public health doctors to provide a questioning voice, a right enshrined in the Acheson report (HC, 1988, p63) and *Duties of a Doctor* (GMC, 1995). The position of EHOs highlights a problem that public health doctors might face if they were to return to local authorities.

Another phase of intersectoral collaboration has begun, however, with the development of local plans to implement the recommendations of the Rio summit, Agenda 21 (ALG, 1995). This has increased the profile of collaborative action, particularly on non-infectious environmental hazards and socio-economic regeneration, and may lead to a strengthening of basic public health functions within councils.

Public health and health promotion must seize this opportunity to learn from the weaknesses of previous programmes and to share information and understanding with the public, using community development techniques coupled with effective strategies for information dissemination. If this strategy proves untenable for public health practitioners in commissioning agencies, then public health will only survive by moving into independent agencies that combine academic and NHS public health expertise. Although there would be a weakening of public health and medical knowledge within the commissioning agency, an organisation in which public health is tied to the office and the demands of the purchasing cycle will, in any case, be unable to improve the health of its population.

A future framework for health promotion

The future for health promotion, both as a discipline and as a range of activities, is mixed. Effective health promotion is a mixture of strategy and policy development, commissioning and direct provision of specific projects and activities; a mixture of specialist and general skills is required (Whitelaw, McKeown, Green, 1995). The main threat to effective action is fragmentation of funding and effort. Health promotion is often isolated from public health across the purchaser-provider divide and, except where health promotion departments come under the banner of public health, health promotion in commissioning agencies comprises isolated individuals. Traditionally, health promotion has had neither the power nor the status to win in conflicts with health authority or trusts over priorities, and is particularly disadvantaged because of the range of its settings: schools, hospital and community trusts, primary care, education, leisure services, neighbourhood and community-based initiatives.

The present diversity of organisational forms is, to some, simply a stage in the development of a mixed economy of health promotion. 'Market testing' of health promotion has been proposed with health service, voluntary sector, private and academic agencies eligible to apply. While external commissioning of specific projects can increase access to particular expertise, it cannot be the sole source of health promotion advice and action. To follow that route would curtail the involvement of health promotion in policy development, in tailoring programmes to the needs of the local population, and in sustaining professional skills and programme quality. There is also a danger that only short-term initiatives would be funded, particularly those with a focus on the individual, since programme evaluation is simpler and attributable change more easily measurable.

To avoid this sort of imbalance in health promotion activity, its teaching and research base must be strengthened. A systematic and rigorous approach to community involvement is required, using research and practice to quantify organisational and individual priorities at neighbourhood level. If a common and mutually supportive approach to evidence, effectiveness, evaluation and audit were developed across public health and health promotion, both would benefit. Systematic review techniques, for example, have shown new audiences that research must be of a high standard if it is to influence policy (Washburn, 1994). Health promotion should be retained as a separate discipline within academic and public health service departments with health promotion expertise included in every public health programme.

Looking backwards, looking forwards

The future relationship between health services and improvements in the public health, and the strategic balance between equity, efficiency, acceptability and sustainability (Creese, 1994), will depend on the vision of health put forward by the government.

Conservative policy is geared to the provision of choice: multi-tiered access to health care through the expansion of private insurance, devolved finance, an extension of the opportunities to accrue short-term benefits associated with NHS funding of private health care, and the flexibility associated with financial sector partnership. The definition of 'health care provided on the basis of need and free at the point of use' is narrowed; the emphasis is on minimal intervention to achieve (centrally defined) acceptable levels of physical and social functioning. Wide inequalities in health would continue to exist but health professionals would fight to minimise the harmful effects of deprivation. Under such policies, where opportunities for health become fragmented, a new vision of equity would develop. Appropriated health measurement tools would be reclaimed: an emphasis on traditional health education, for example, would increase application of traditional risk factors as markers for health improvement (Kelleher, 1995). Consumerism would become refashioned as user involvement through initiatives designed to enhance involvement in commissioning and service development and in empowering people to achieve full benefit from prevention and treatment services. Eventually, even Conservative policymakers would recognise the limitations of individually based, privately funded attempts to improve health.

The Labour Party must focus now on the building blocks of its future health strategy. A market approach to health and health care is neither egalitarian nor efficient. Health is a resource and health care a source of employment and innovation. Neither should be squandered.

One legacy of the Conservative government, however, is

the growth in private health insurance. This is one measure of the additional health care funding that could be reappropriated by the NHS and allocated more efficiently and more effectively. These funds could be used to pump prime services for people of working age as part of an interdepartmental drive to reduce the barriers to employment faced by people with disability, acute or chronic illness. The health service role would be to reduce time away from work, using the popularity of early evening and Saturday out-patient and operating facilities, but targeting their use towards those most likely to benefit; those least likely to have paid time off for hospital appointments, or whose employment is most insecure. This group comprises not only those in recent or temporary employment but also a cohort of junior and middle management, many of whom seem unaware that they are longer protected, either by nationally agreed terms and conditions of service or by union membership.

A Minister for Public Health

The slow progress towards (and in some cases away from) *Health of the Nation* targets, highlights not only the inability of the NHSE to influence important determinants of public health, but also the lack of co-ordinated action across government departments. Traditionally, the Secretary of State for Health has been responsible for the provision of health care for individuals, and political survival dictates that this remains the highest priority for ministers. Despite the relatively minor health benefits that accrue from many intensive interventions, there has been little political will to counteract the technological determinism of a health care market led by opportunity and demand for intervention (Anderson, 1995). Instead, the publicised concerns of ministers, despite their conversion to evidence-based care, have often revolved around limiting access to services on financial or social grounds unrelated to ability to benefit.

Long-term, sustainable improvement in the health of Britain requires a balance between population and individual interventions, similar to that required at local level. Development and implementation of policy to achieve this requires a minister for public health, able to set out a clear vision of health improvement for all and mobilise broad political support for progressive public health strategies.

Financial strategies

The Minister for Public Health will have a responsibility to ensure that the core funding of the health service can produce measurable improvements in those health targets given highest priority. Financial decision-making, like other decisions in the health service, should be based on best available evidence of benefit. Funding must also produce sustainable improvement: the minister must have the flexibility to use cost and efficiency targets, not as ends in themselves, but as tools to help design effective organisations.

This public health financial strategy must then be implemented at all layers of the health service. Policy implementation must be costed, strategic funding plans developed and agreed. This will require a commitment to core NHS funding for periods of longer than one year at a time. Specific investment is required to reduce waste and to improve the effectiveness of public health action. Ministers can act to rationalise the publication, briefing and dissemination of key knowledge; at local level, a structured programme of investment is required. A strategy of this kind would raise the quality of public health action across the country to that of the best, rather than redistributing resources and expertise to bring the best down to the level of the average.

Organisational strategies for implementing public health policy

The development and implementation of public health policy requires that a dynamic balance is achieved between current wisdom, critical appraisal of the evidence for change, and the pace at which change can be accepted. Any review of the arrangements for managing the health service to achieve public health goals must include a commitment to organisational development, procedural review, and development of explicit standards for expert contributions. The strength of a professional civil service - independence from the minister - should be exploited and the quality of advice in policymaking, the drafting of guidance and legislation and the pace of business made explicit. Standards set by a minister for public health would emphasise outcome measures and the requirement for clinical audit and continuing education and development among professionally qualified civil servants.

In setting objectives, the minister must ensure that they are shared and compatible, both across initiatives and across aspects of government. Currently the NHSE sets corporate contract priorities for health agencies; these may conflict with the professional objectives set through the Chief Medical Officer or become unachievable when taken together. The relationship between the CMO, directors of public health and the medical director of the NHSE must be resolved and a single set of objectives developed. At all levels the purpose of health care management should be the development and achievement of specific targets for health improvement; tactics may vary across the service, but not aims.

The abolition of regional health authorities and the development of the regional offices of the NHSE will not facilitate the development of a shared agenda and objectives. A regional structure could provide named links between the NHSE, Department of Health, chief executives of health agencies and trusts, directors of public health and medical directors, chairs of fundholding and primary care commissioning groups. The aim would be to achieve more efficient and effective use of existing networks, minimising the requirement for paper directives and monitoring. The role would include overseeing the piloting of developments, reviewing services, and the evaluation of specific initiatives. Progress towards national targets should be assessed using fewer, unambiguous and measurable objectives set within a framework that allows clear options for local interpretation and communication of necessary refinements back to the centre.

When the structure for delivering health improvements is in place, the minister for public health should establish programmes designed to deliver improvements initially in the processes by which policy decisions are taken. The first programme should be a comprehensive programme of education and training for NHS managers in the public health objectives of a national health service; the aim here should be to help identify and address key health problems. The relationship between health, health care and effective intervention should be examined, using, for example, housing, employment legislation, transport, accidents and income to emphasise the complementary role of evidence-based interventions at the level of the population and the individual (Mackenbach, 1995).

The second area for attention should be research, development, and the implementation and dissemination of knowledge. A systematic and rolling programme of appraisal of the strengths and weaknesses of the evidence for specific interventions should be undertaken.

The third priority is to champion public health in the UK, establishing specific programmes to maintain its strengths and develop public health expertise. The links between national and local action are exemplified by communicable disease surveillance, the mobilisation of a comprehensive response to HIV/AIDS (McKee, 1995), the recording and analysis of secular trends, and the detailed studies undertaken by the Office of Population Censuses and Surveys (OPCS). The techniques of communicable disease surveillance could be used to tackle other public health problems of similar magnitude, such as environmental hazards (Ayres, 1995). Success at local level could be used to disseminate effective methods to improve health at community level and to formalise the role of the voluntary sector in public health programmes. The National Childbirth Trust, for example, provides an evidence-based consumer perspective on interventions aimed at improving the health of pregnant women and families with young children.

The fourth priority requires the greatest investment of vision, time, people and perseverance. Rebuilding health as a communal responsibility requires the commitment to work across agencies to empower primary care, and to revise and refine the balance between medical, social and environmental models of health with local authorities, voluntary agencies and communities. Sharing this vision of development will, however, increase the prospect of improving health for the many, not for the few.

Priorities for implementation include changes in the distribution of tax revenue, for example banning tobacco advertising and using revenue from tobacco sales to fund health promotion initiatives. This technique has been used effectively in Australia, complemented by public health sponsorship (Powles, Gifford, 1993). The proposed reorganisation of the civil service would streamline the health promotion effort. The HEA, for example, could become a Healthy England steering group, with similar groups driving the efforts of bodies in Wales, Scotland and Northern Ireland. This would co-ordinate action between health promotion and public health at highest level.

Incremental changes in the way that health care is organised and delivered would reflect in the implementation of these programmes. The health service in Northern Ireland, with its model of strategic and operational integration of health with social services, could become a flagship for health improvement. Its poor health record, for example in death from cardiovascular disease, reflects the potential health gains to be made from concerted action, rather than a failure of the integration.

A minister for public health would also make clear the commitment to improving health at both national and international levels, enabling full participation in EU public health and health promotion directives, including Article 129 of the Maastricht Treaty, and providing formal opportunities for learning, collaboration and research across the EU and European Economic Area. The leadership provided by such an initiative would advance the health debate in Britain beyond party political argument over the balance between individual expectations, population benefit and short-term savings. Managers responsible for setting policy and budgets would be required to demonstrate how their short-term action plans would contribute to effective long-term resource allocation rather than meeting the current requirement to break even annually. These would be tangible steps towards the development of sustainable health policy. The ultimate aim is clear: to engender public allegiance to a vision of a healthier future while ensuring that measurable and attainable targets for long-term health improvement are set for the first time. These should be set out as a contract with the country, renewable by agreement.

References

Abelin T., Brzezinski Z. J., Carstairs V. D. L., *Measurement in Health Promotion and Protection*, WHO, Geneva 1987.

ALG, *Setting the Agenda for London. Developing a local Agenda 21: towards a sustainable future for London in the 21st Century*, ALG, London 1995.

Anderson O.W., 'The health services establishment is becoming an independent variable: a life of its own', *Medical Care Research and Review*, 52, 1995, pp6-33.

Ashton J., 'The origins of *Healthy Cities*' in Ashton J. (ed), *Healthy Cities*, Open University Press, Milton Keynes 1992.

Ayres P. J., 'Major chemical incidents - a response, the role of the Consultant in Communicable Disease Control and the case of need for a national surveillance-resource centre', *Journal of Public Health Medicine*, 17, 1995, pp164-170.

Bayley T., Browse N., Kilpatrick R., Macara A., Richards P., Turnberg L., *Core Values for the Medical Profession in the 21st Century*, BMA, London 1995.

Begay M. E., Traynor M., Glantz S. A., 'The tobacco industry, state politics and tobacco education in California', *American Journal of Public Health*, 83(9), 1993, pp1214-21.

Ben Shlomo Y., 'The health of the nation: all aboard the merry-go-round', *Critical Public Health*, No 4, 1991, pp24-30.

Campbell D. M., Braddick M. R., Stewart S., 'Public health advice to local authorities: does it happen?' *Public Health*, 108, 1994, pp313-18.

Creese A., 'Global trends in health care reform', *World Health Forum*, 15, 1994, pp317-22.

Declich S., Carter A. O., 'Public health surveillance: historical origin, methods and evaluation', *Bulletin of the World Health Organisation*, 72, 1994, pp285-304.

Dekker E., 'Health care reforms and public health', *European Journal of Public Health*, 4, 1994, pp281-86.

Department of Health, *Health Authority Public Health Functions*, HC (88) 63.

Department of Health, *The Health of the Nation: a strategy for health in England*, HMSO, London 1992.

Department of Health, *The Health of the Nation. Variations in Health. What can the Department of Health and the NHS do?* HMSO, London 1995.

Department of Health and Social Security, *Inequalities in Health: report of a working group*, DHSS, London 1980.

Duncan T., 'Community Councils Participation in the Healthy Cities Project in Glasgow, November 1990', *Research for Health for All: the Healthy City and its evaluation*, 4-5 April 1991, Glasgow.

Faculty of Public Health Medicine, *Strategies for Health Promotion in Primary Care*, Faculty of Public Health Medicine, London December 1993.

Field M.G., 'Introduction' in McKinlay J. B. (ed), *Contemporary issues in Health, Medicine and Social Policy. Success and crisis in national health systems*, Routledge, London 1989.

Flynn P., 'Measuring health in cities' in Ashton J. (ed), *Healthy Cities*, Open University Press, Milton Keynes 1992.

Gill L., Goldacre M., Simmons H., Bettley G., Griffith M., 'Computerised linking of medical records: methodological guidance', *Journal of Epidemiology and Community Health*, 47, 1993, pp316-19.

Grace V.M., 'The marketing of empowerment and the construction of the health consumer: a critique of health promotion', *International Journal of Health Services*, 1991; 21(2): 329-43.

Green L. W., 'Who will qualify to fill positions in health promotion?' *Canadian Journal of Public Health*, 86, 1995, pp7-9.

Harrison A. (ed), 'Part 1. Main events. Health Policy Review 1992/93' *Health Care UK 1992/93*, King's Fund Institute, London 1993.

Health Education Authority, *Investing in Health*, Health Education Authority Annual Report 1994/95, HMSO, London 1995.

Hennesy C. H., Moriarty D. G., Zack M. M., Scherr P. A., Brackbill R., 'Measuring health related quality of life for public health surveillance', *Public health reports*, 1994, pp65-72.

Kelleher C., 'Health promotion: shades of Lewis Carroll', *Journal of Epidemiology and Community Health*, 49, 1995, pp1-4.

Klein R., 'The goals of health policy: church or garage?' Health Policy Review 1992/93, *Health Care UK 1992/93*, King's Fund Institute, London 1993.

Suffolk Health Authority, Mid Anglia Community Trust, *Community Outcomes and Resource Groups Initiatives in Suffolk. Feasibility Report*, Suffolk Health Authority, Mid Anglia Community Trust, Suffolk 1994.

Kunst A. E., Mackenbach J. P., 'International variation in the size of mortality differences associated with occupational status', *International Journal of Epidemiology*, 23, 1994, pp742-50.

Mackenbach J. P., 'Tackling inequalities in health', *BMJ*, 310, 1995, pp1152-3.

Mackenbach J.P., 'Socio-economic inequalities in health in the Netherlands: impact of a five year programme', *BMJ*, 309, pp1487-91.

Mackenbach J. P., 'Socio-economic health differences in the Netherlands: a review of recent empirical findings', *Social Science and Medicine*, 34, 1992, pp213-16.

Mackenbach J. P., van den Bos J., Joung I. M. A., van de Mheen H., Stronks K., 'The determinants of excellent health: different from the determinants of ill-health?' International Journal of Epidemiology, 23 1994, pp1273-81.

Miller Jones A., Simpson A., Wilson S., 'Healthy prospects for Kings Cross?' *Critical Public Health*,(4), 1991, pp15-20.

McKee M., '2020 vision', *Journal of Public Health Medicine*, 17, 1995 pp127-31.

Moore W., 'Fit to drop', *Health Service Journal*, 20 October 1994.

Nance A. J., 'A space in which to care: clinical psychology in an age of conservatism', *Critical Public Health*, 3(2), 1992, pp30-35.

NHS Management Executive, *Public Health: responsibilities of the NHS and the roles of others*, (Abrams Report), HSG 56, 1993.

Osler M., 'Social class and health behaviour in Danish adults: a longitudinal study', *Public Health*, 107, 1993, pp251-60.

Owikel J. G., 'After epidemiological research: what next? Community action for health promotion', *Public Health Reviews*, 22, 1994, pp375-94.

Phillimore P., Beattie A., Townsend P., 'Widening inequality of health in Northern England', *BMJ*, 308, 1994, pp1125-28.

Powles J. W., Gifford S., 'Health of nations, lessons from Victoria, Australia', *BMJ*, 306, 1993, pp125-27.

Quam L., 'Improving clinical effectiveness in the NHS: an alternative to the white paper', *BMJ*, 299, 1989, pp448-50.

Rathwell T., 'Realities of Health for All by the year 2000', *Social Science and Medicine*, 35(4), 1992, pp541-47.

Robine J. M., Ritchie K., 'Healthy life expectancy: evaluation of global indicator of change in population health' *BMJ*, 302, 1991, pp457-60.

Sacco R. L., 'Risk factors and outcomes for ischaemic stroke', *Neurology*, 45(2 suppl 1), 1995, S10-S14.

Sallis J. F., McKenzie T. L., 'Physical education's role in public health', *Research Quarterly for Exercise and Sport*, 62(2), 1991, pp124-37.

Scambler G., Goraya A., 'Movements for health: the new public health agenda', *Critical Public Health*, 5(2), 1994, pp4-10.

Stevens A., Colin-Jones D., Gabbay J., '"Quick and clean": authoritative health technology assessment for local health care contracting', *Health Trends*, 27, 1995, pp37-42.

Stevenson H. M., Burke M., 'Bureaucratic logic in new social movement clothing: the limits of health promotion research', *Canadian Journal of Public Health*, 83 suppl1: S47-53, 1992.

Sutton G. C., 'Health for all by the year 1990? Part two: Primary care and environmental aspects', *Journal of Public Health Medicine*, 16, 1994, pp195-99.

Toon P. D., 'Health checks in general practice', *BMJ*, 310, 1995, pp1083-84.

Van den Bos G. A. M., Limburg L. C. M., 'Public health and chronic diseases', *European Journal of Public Health*, 5, 1991, pp1-2.

Washburn E. P., Orza M. J., Berlin J. A., Nicholson W. J., Todd A.C., Frumkin H., Chalmers T. C., 'Residual proximity to electricity transmission and distribution equipment and risk of childhood leukaemia, childhood lymphoma, and childhood nervous system tumours; systematic review, evaluation, and meta-analysis', *Cancer Causes and Control*, 5 1994, pp299-309.

Whitelaw S., McKeown K., Green F., 'Market testing specialist health promotion services - a test case for an imaginative public health presence in purchasing', *Journal of Public Health Medicine*, 17, 1995, pp211-16.

World Health Organisation Regional Office for Europe, Copenhagen, *Health for all targets. The health policy for Europe*, European Health

DEMOCRACY, ACCOUNTABILITY AND CONSUMERISM

David J Hunter and Stephen Harrison

This chapter focuses on democracy, accountability and consumerism in the context of the UK National Health Service (NHS); it is divided into four main sections. First of all we examine here why it is that these matters are issues, discuss the concepts themselves, and note that there may be a conflict between democratic accountability and consumer accountability. In the second section, we give a historical perspective on the changing ways in which the NHS has handled these matters to date, and in the third we ask whether or not such matters are of real importance. The final section presents a range of options, and their relative merits, for the future.

We begin from the premise that health care is not just another service commodity such as motor vehicle repair, plumbing, hairdressing, or accountancy. One way of looking at this is to note the apparently widespread belief (not only in Britain) that citizens should not have to pay out of pocket for their health care, but rather through the tax or social insurance system. Such a view is presumably underpinned by some sort of combination of rational self-interest ('I might become sick and be unable to afford care') and altruism ('people's life chances may be fundamentally affected by ill-health and care ought therefore to be available as of right'). There are of course problems with this view; motor vehicle repair and plumbing may offer a significant contribution to health and life chances, and the NHS does not provide care as of statutory right (see below). Nevertheless, it seems likely that some mix of the above views underpins the very widespread public support which the NHS enjoys (Harrison, 1988, pp88-9; Jowett et al, 1991).

An alternative way of approaching this phenomenon is to

say that the public funding of health care in Britain is the product of history; other choices could, in principle at least, have been made about how to improve the health and life chances of the citizenry. Some such choices were made at the time of the creation of the NHS (publicly-funded education, for instance) but others, such as publicly-funded motor vehicle repair, or a radical redistribution of income and wealth, were not. But whether one thinks of the publicly-funded NHS as having been arrived at for rational or irrational reasons, the situation is that it exists, and this fact raises questions about democracy, accountability and consumerism.

CITIZENS, TAXPAYERS AND USERS

Although the balance of emphasis between the two has shifted backwards and forwards over time, citizenship involves both rights and duties (Roche, 1992, p4). In the context of a national health service, one might say that citizens have a duty to pay taxes (within their assessed liabilities) and the right to use services (within their assessed need). In principle, both rights and duties are continuous but may not seem so in practice; it is unlikely that a person's lifetime tax contributions to the NHS and his/her usage of services will balance out. In the extreme, some people may never earn enough to pay taxes yet be 'chronic' users of services due to long-term disability (two things which may, of course, be connected), while others are fortunate enough to earn a great deal of money while remaining healthy. Indeed the whole rationale of a national health service is to socialise the financial risk of ill-health; if payment and usage by each individual were actually likely to balance out over a lifetime much of the point of organising health care in this way would be lost, and right-wing alternatives such as personal 'medical savings accounts' (Greene, 1995) would become less unattractive.

It follows from all this that the interests of (some) taxpayers are likely to conflict with those of (some) users. For instance, the former might not wish public health expenditure to grow to the extent that taxation increases are required, while the latter might be very much in favour of the rapid development of services. Another example might be the preference of the former for services likely to be needed by all, or most, people in their lifetime, whereas the latter might have minority preferences for services which address their own health condition: perhaps *in vitro* fertilisation, or plastic surgery to remove tattoos - both of which have been argued by some health authorities to be of low priority (Harrison and Wistow, 1992) - or treatment for sickle-cell anaemia (which affects particular ethnic minorities). One implication of all this is that the notion of 'consumerism', which might be appropriate to a market in which individuals make purchasing decisions involving personal direct expenditures, is inappropriate for our discussion; the NHS consumer can only be sovereign at someone else's expense. For this reason, we have preferred to refer to 'users' throughout the chapter, and our use of the term 'consumerism' should be understood in this non-market context. Nevertheless, health care services do purport to be personal services, implying that the interests of users do have a legitimate claim to consideration in the organisation and operation of the NHS.

Although the potential clash of interest between citizens and users cannot be eliminated, it needs to be balanced in some way. One way of approaching this problem is through different dimensions of the concept of accountability.

THE DIMENSIONS OF ACCOUNTABILITY

According to Day and Klein's (1987) study of accountability in the public service, the core notion of political accountability involves a continuing obligation on the part of those to whom government is entrusted to explain and justify their conduct to citizens (p7). However, the massive complexity of contemporary government is far beyond that of the contexts in which our notions of democracy and accountability were developed, implying the need to harness managerial accountability to political accountability (p9). In principle, it is straightforward to distinguish between these two dimensions of accountability. *Political accountability* involves criteria of judgement which are contestable and can therefore only be discharged by explanation and justification rather than against objective standards. In contrast, *managerial accountability* can be discharged by demonstrating that agreed tasks have been carried out to agreed standards and is therefore ostensibly more technical than political. Managerial accountability can be subdivided into fiscal accountability (for incurring expenditure only in accordance with the rules), process accountability (for acting as specified and obtaining value for money), and programme accountability (for ensuring that the action achieves its intended outcome) (Day and Klein, 1987, pp26-7).

This distinction between political and managerial accountability can be related to the distinction which we drew earlier between citizens and users; we might say that political accountability should involve the interests of all citizens, while certain aspects of managerial accountability (that is, for delivering the required processes and outcomes) might focus on users' interests. Indeed, this is our position in general terms. However, matters are not so straightforward for, as Day and Klein (1987, pp4, 28) note, the practical application of a neat distinction between political and managerial accountability rests upon four questionable assumptions. The first is that the current political arrangements provide *continuing* explanation and justification of public policy and activity; in other words, democracy and accountability are not identical and the former is not a sufficient condition for the latter, though it may be a necessary one. Thus the suggestion that health authority members ought be elected (Ham, 1985) is insufficient of itself to ensure political accountability.

The second and third assumptions are that there are effective links between the processes of political and managerial accountability and that political processes generate decisions that include clear-cut objectives and criteria that can be acted upon by managers. In practice, the opposite may be the case. Politicians may prefer not to make themselves hostages to fortune by stating clear objectives, nor to run the risk of alienating sections of the electorate by articulating clear priorities and non-priorities (Pollitt and Harrison, 1994, pp4-5). The final assumption is that managers can reasonably be asked to account for the activities of those who actually deliver public services. In the context of the NHS, this means doctors and other clinical professionals over whom managers can have little detailed control (for a discussion of 'clinical freedom', see Harrison, 1995) and compared with whom managers are relatively unpopular with the public (Harrison, 1988, p89). In general, numerous studies of public policy in a range of contexts have shown that 'implementation' consists of much more than technical activities in pursuit of policy objectives (Pressman and Wildavsky, 1979).

THE REQUIREMENTS OF ACCOUNTABILITY IN THE NHS

We will end this chapter by proposing an alternative mechanism by which NHS accountability might in the future be secured. At this point, however, it is appropriate to set out the implications of the preceding analysis for such mechanisms. Our first conclusion is that there is no simple recipe for allocating political and managerial accountability within and between public institutions; rather, accountability needs to become pervasive within such institutions; 'woven into the fabric of political and social life' (Day and Klein, 1987, p249). Secondly, whatever arrangements exist must be capable of recognising and balancing the potential conflict of interest between citizens and users. Thirdly, such arrangements must be based on the principle of continuous visibility rather than solely upon the mode of selection of authority members or officers. Fourth, those who are accountable must have effective control of service providers; if managers cannot exercise this, then tighter internal control by the professions themselves is implied (Day and Klein, 1987, p248).

A BRIEF HISTORY OF ACCOUNTABILITY IN THE NHS

In this section we consider the changing ways in which the NHS has reflected democracy and accountability since its inception. In order to do so it is necessary to examine both the formal arrangements such as membership of the relevant statutory authorities, and the style of internal management of the service. We shall see that, throughout the period, the responsibility of statutory (health) authorities to elected central government has provided the main mechanism of formal democratic legitimacy. However, such authorities have never been in any substantial sense representative of citizens, nor functioned as the locus of power within the NHS; medical professionals have dominated for most of the Service's history, though this has been challenged in recent years by the increased influence of managers.

1948 TO 1973

Although the wartime coalition government's plans for a post-war health service (the Willink plan) had involved its governance by joint boards of existing local government authorities (Foot, 1973, p109), and despite the Labour Party's initial preference for direct democracy (Willcocks, 1967, p62) and Morrison's concerns at the potential undermining of elected local government (Webster, 1988, p85), the 1945 Labour government gave only what today would be referred to as community services, together with ambulance services, to the latter. The two remaining elements of the tripartite NHS, the hospitals and family (medical, dental, pharmaceutical and optical) practitioners, were governed by appointed bodies. According to the NHS's official historian:

> Bevan realised that imperfections in the current system of local government fundamentally undermined schemes for municipalising health services ... nationalisation [of the hospitals] offered an opportunity to evolve a more rational geographical framework, and a chance to create a system of administration that would be more palatable to the [medical] profession and the voluntary lobby. Bevan held out the attraction of 'worker control' to the profession and to health workers as one of the positive merits of hospital nationalisation and indeed of nationalisation in general (Webster, 1988, p83).

Bevan's biographer emphasised a slightly different rationale; the legal basis of the new NHS in the minister's *duty* to provide a comprehensive health service implied ministerial *power* to deliver (Foot, 1973, p192). Bevan himself seems to have been fond of emphasising direct ministerial responsibility as a virtue. He made more than one speech on this theme, famously remarking on one occasion in 1946:

> the Minister of Health will be a whipping-boy for the Health Service in Parliament. Every time a maid kicks over a bucket of slops in a ward an agonised wail will go through Whitehall. After the new Service is introduced there will be a cacophony of complaints. The newspapers will be full of them ... For a while it will appear that everything is going wrong. As a matter of fact, everything will be going right, because people will be able effectively to complain (quoted in Foot, 1973, pp192-3).

In the years of preparation for the NHS, between 1945 and 1948, great care seems to have been taken to reassure potential critics about the new arrangements; local authority associations were promised representation on Regional Hospital Boards (RHBs) and Executive Councils (ECs), the TUC was promised representation on RHBs and hospital doctors were promised a voice at all levels (Webster, 1988, pp89-90), though the BMA was refused direct nominations to Hospital Management Committees (HMCs) (Webster, 1988, p169). In December 1947 Bevan enquired rhetorically of the BMA whether they would prefer to have local authorities, or the Minister, in charge (Foot, 1973, p169).

The 1946 National Health Service Act required the new authorities 'to administer the service consistent with the directives of the Minister and relevant regulations' (Webster, 1988, p95). The mechanisms of appointment to the new bodies were as follows. In respect of non-teaching hospitals, the minister appointed the chairs of RHBs and, after various consultations, the rest of the Board. The RHB then recommended the disposition of hospital groupings within the region and, when these were approved by the minister, appointed the chairs and members of HMCs (Webster, 1988, p274). In respect of teaching hospitals, boards of governors were agents of the minister and appointed by him: one-fifth from universities, medical schools and RHBs respectively, with the remainder chosen after consultation with local authorities and other interests (Webster, 1988, p271). The BMA had unsuccessfully sought for HMCs and boards of governors to appoint their own chairs (Webster, 1988, p129) and unsuccessful proposals had been made for payment for chairs and members (Webster, 1988, p277).

The outcome of these appointments, representing 'the elite of available voluntary effort', was heavy representation of the establishment (of the original 14 RHB chairs, seven were businessmen, four were professionals, and only three had Labour Party or union connections: Webster, 1988, p274), and pervasive representation of the medical profession. Overall medical representation on RHBs was 29 per cent in 1947, rising to 31 per cent in 1956, and on some individual HMCs approached 50 per cent (Webster, 1988, pp276, 281). Trade union/Labour Party representation was much lower than local authorities and unions felt that they had been led to expect, and TUC nominees employed in the hospital service were debarred on the grounds that the TUC was consulted not on behalf of health workers, but as a proxy for consumers more generally (Webster, 1988, p278). The boards were far from demographically representative of the population, having a strong bias in favour of men and persons over 60 years of age (Webster, 1988, p276).

In the primary care field, the composition of Executive Councils, which caused little controversy, was finely balanced between professional representatives (seven from the Local Medical Committee, three from the Local Dental Committee and two from the Local Pharmaceutical Committee) and government appointees (five plus the chair by the Minister, eight by the relevant local government health authorities) (Webster, 1988, pp348-9).

The performance of the various boards and committees seems to have been fairly undistinguished; for instance there was a relatively small core of activists (sometimes having poor relationships with their colleagues), attendance was often poor, performance unmeasured, and (perhaps as a result) power tended to be assumed by officers and sub-committees (Webster, 1988, pp276-7). It has already been noted that members of the various health authorities were neither sociologically nor syndically representative, nor (other than in the case of the local health authorities who governed community and ambulance services) were they democratically representative except in the rather tenuous sense that many were appointed by a minister who was himself an elected politician. The Guillebaud Commission of 1953 to 1956 rejected the transfer of the NHS to local government (Committee of Enquiry, 1956). Moreover, many key issues in the new Service were dealt with, and indeed continue to be dealt with at the time of writing, through various joint committees of the medical profession and government appointees; examples of these corporatist arrangements are those for determining hospital medical posts (Harrison *et al*, 1990, ch.4) and the location of general practices (Levitt and Wall, 1984, p176).

1974 TO 1990

The run-up to the reorganisation of 1974 was, like that to the creation of the Service, marked by discussion of a number of alternative schemes (for a brief review, see Levitt and Wall, 1984, pp12-7), including two proposals that the NHS should be wholly governed by the new local government authorities (Royal Commission, 1969; Department of Health and Social Security, 1970) since planning for a reorganisation of local government was proceeding in parallel. In the event, the form of organisation decided upon took the form of a partial unification of the three parts of the tripartite structure. Appointed Regional Health Authorities (RHAs) and Area Health Authorities (AHAs) would be responsible for hospital and community services (the latter, therefore, being 'lost' by local authorities) while Executive Councils would become Family Practitioner Committees (FPCs) with a formal link to, though not controlled by, AHAs. Since the detailed plans for the design of the new Service had been made by a Conservative government but implemented by the Labour government elected in early 1974, some modifications were soon made to the original constitution of authorities. The Conservative Secretary of State, Sir Keith Joseph, had wanted their selection to be on grounds of 'management ability' (Klein, 1983, p96), while his Labour successor, Mrs Barbara Castle, had desired greater democracy, through a large increase of local authority representatives on RHAs and AHAs (Levitt, 1979, pp57-8) and perhaps through the election to AHAs by their colleagues of two worker representatives (Royal Commission, 1979, p328). In the event, only minor changes to these constitutions were made between 1974 and 1982.

The (part-time) chairs and members of the new RHAs were appointed by the Secretary of State (the title used in respect of the most senior ministers after 1968) after consultation with the professions, local authorities, universities, trade unions and voluntary bodies (Levitt and Wall, 1984, p50). The new AHAs also had part-time chairs appointed by the Secretary of State. Their original membership included nominees of the relevant local authorities (the nominees were not themselves required to be elected councillors), at least one nominee of the relevant university with a medical school, and the balance (including a hospital consultant, a GP, and a nurse) appointed by the RHA (Levitt, 1976, p57). Since the GP would be self-employed and the consultant employed by the RHA, these medical members were allowed to sit on the authorities in whose area they worked. The nurse member, however, had to work in a different area. 1974 also saw the beginning of the end of Bevan's voluntary principle in that the chairs of the new HAs received an honorarium for their efforts (Levitt, 1976, p57).

As noted above, this scheme of membership, inherited from the Conservatives, was regarded by the Labour government as insufficiently democratic (Castle, 1980, p242). In its consultative document *Democracy in the National Health Service* (Department of Health and Social Security, 1974) it proposed that one-third of RHA and DHA members should be drawn from local government, that Community Health Councils (CHCs - see below) should provide two members of each AHA, and that two members of NHS non-medical, non-nursing staff should serve on AHAs (Levitt, 1976, p58). In 1975, after consultation on the document, it was decided that such changes would be implemented on a progressive basis from 1977, though with only a single CHC representative with only speaking (not voting) rights (Levitt, 1976, p58). In the event the staff nominees were never introduced.

A Royal Commission on the NHS established in 1976 by the Labour government reported in 1979, after the election of the first Thatcher Conservative government in May of that year; *inter alia* it rejected the notion of elected single-purpose health authorities (Royal Commission, 1979, p329) and suggested that the Service might have a superfluous tier of organisation, though without specifying whether it should be the statutory AHA or the lower hierarchical level of purely administrative districts that should be abolished (1979, p324). In the event, AHAs were dispensed with and, from 1982, replaced with statutory District Health Authorities (DHAs).

The membership of DHAs was not dissimilar to that of their predecessors: a part-time salaried chair (nominally two days per week), one hospital consultant, one GP, one nurse, midwife or health visitor, one trade unionist nominated by the Trades Council (and not an NHS employee), one nominee of the relevant medical school, at least four nominees of the relevant local government authority(ies), and at least seven generalists (Levitt *et al*, 1995, p67). As had been the case with all hospital authorities since 1948 and with health authorities since 1974, members were ostensibly representatives of the community at large (Klein, 1983, p96) despite the professional or partisan bases of some of their nominations (Levitt and Wall, 1984, p21). Whether or not it was realistic to expect detachment on the part of persons so nominated, it is worth noting that an entirely different principle had since 1974 applied to the construction of the management teams which ran districts on a day-to-day basis; in what can only be described as a manifestation of medical syndicalism, District Management Teams included a hospital consultant and a GP, each elected by his or her respective colleagues and equal in status to the full-time chief officers (Klein, 1983, p95).

As noted above, the role of the former Executive Councils was taken over by FPCs after the 1974 reorganisation. The fine balance of their predecessors was maintained, with eleven members nominated by the health authority, four by the local authority, eight by the Local Medical Committee, three by the Local Dental Committee, and two each by the Local Optical and Pharmaceutical Committees (Levitt and Wall, 1984, pp67-8). After the abolition of AHAs in 1982 FPCs, restyled as Family Health Service Authorities (FHSAs) gained independence from other local health governance arrangements and became responsible directly to the Department of Health. Unlike other authorities FPCs/FHSAs were not required to hold public meetings until 1983 (Allsop and May, 1986, p30).

The 1974 reorganisation had involved one important break with earlier NHS governance arrangements; HMC and local health committees had been assumed to be responsible both for managing the service and for representing the user and public interest and some members of such authorities had chosen to take, albeit rather ineffectively, a user viewpoint (Levitt and Wall, 1984, p254). Under the new arrangements, AHAs (and their successors) were appointed with specific *management* responsibilities (Levitt and Wall, 1984, p254) in the then prevailing belief that there would otherwise be a dangerous confusion of roles as had contributed, for instance, to the 1969 scandal over mistreatment of patients at Ely Hospital (Klein and Lewis, 1976, pp14-15). The new authorities were smaller than the old HMCs, with the result that lay participation was much reduced; it became necessary, in an era of political populism, to provide a mechanism for the restoration of local participation (Klein and Lewis, 1976, p13). And so Community Health Councils (CHCs) came to be

invented almost by accident because, when the plans for a reorganised [NHS] were almost complete, all those involved realised that something was missing: an element which could be ... seen as providing a degree of local democracy, consumer participation or public involvement (Klein and Lewis, 1976, p11).

The CHCs, one for each district, had the role of representing the views of local users to the relevant health authorities (Levitt and Wall, 1984, p254). Half of the membership was nominated by local government authorities, one-third by voluntary organisations, and the remaining one-sixth by RHAs; CHCs also had powers to co-opt additional members (Levitt and Wall, 1984, pp254-5) and select their own chairpersons (Hallas, 1976, p13). The early members of CHCs were not sociologically or demographically representative of the population; the middle-aged, the middle class and the male sex were over-represented nationally, though not to the same extent in every region (Klein and Lewis, 1976, pp29-36). Although CHCs had some significant powers (most notably to compel AHAs' proposals to close hospitals to be referred for ministerial determination), and some important successes for individual patients, it has in general been hard to show a significant impact overall (Hallas, 1976, p59; Klein and Lewis, 1976, p135; Ham, 1980, p226; Schulz and Harrison, 1983, pp30-3; Lee and Mills, 1982, p142).

Taken overall, the period 1974 to 1990 manifested a bewildering variety of piecemeal changes to the formal arrangements for the governance of the NHS. Although comprehensive data does not seem to be available it is unlikely that the membership of health authorities in this period was any more sociologically or demographically representative than in the preceding period. Yet it is clear that, on the part of the Labour governments at least, there was an attempt to be more pluralistic, that is to draw membership from a wider range of sources. This, however, left a central paradox: if the arrangements for securing members were largely defined in terms of the *institutions* from which they were to be drawn, it would be difficult in practice to expect them to behave as individuals and not in some sense to represent (for instance) their profession, political party or university. (For a more extended discussion, see Levitt, 1976, pp58-60.) At the same time, it is difficult to see how accountability (especially financial accountability) to the political centre could be consonant with representativeness to other institutions (Klein and Lewis, 1976, p13). This paradox did not always lead to problems and Levitt *et al* (1995, p66) note that most health authorities did not conduct themselves in a party political fashion, even in respect of such highly ideological matters as private practice. Nevertheless, from 1983 onwards there were a number of DHAs which resisted central government policies on financial and staffing limits (Levitt *et al*, 1995, p67), a practice which may well have contributed to the eventual demise of RHAs and of DHAs in the form they then took (see below).

This fundamental incoherence suggests, therefore, that the architects of future arrangements need to pay greater attention to the relationship between the mode of selection of members and their prescribed role and accountabilities. We return to this in our final main section.

1991 AND AFTER

Indeed, the governance arrangements which accompanied the implementation, from 1991 onwards, of the organisational changes proposed in *Working for Patients* (arrangements which are still in operation at the time of writing) do display greater coherence in rejecting pluralism in order to emphasise authority members' personal contributions; as the white paper itself put it,

> At present [health authorities] ... are neither truly representative nor management bodies. Many members, such as those appointed directly by local authorities or on the advice of trade unions and professional bodies *usually regard themselves as representatives*. But as a body they are often confronted by the need to take detailed decisions on key management issues. And the actual managers themselves are not members of the authority. The government believes that authorities based on this confusion of roles would not be equipped to handle the complex managerial and contractual issues that the new system of matching resources to

performance will demand. The members needed to work in the new system should be appointed on the strength of the skills and experience they can bring to an authority's work. (Department of Health *et al*, 1989, pp64-5; emphasis added).

These words heralded a move, which took effect in April 1991, towards a system of NHS governance based on the commercial model of a board of directors. The new model provided for RHAs, DHAs and the new 'trusts' (which were to run hospitals and community services) to have a non-executive chair (appointed by the Secretary of State), and equal numbers of executive and non-executive directors. The former were the full-time salaried chief officers, including the general manager (later re-styled as chief executives) and finance director. The latter were part-time (and salaried accordingly); RHA non-executives, including an FHSA chairperson (see below) were appointed by the Secretary of State, and DHA and trust non-executives by the RHA (Ham, 1990).

Not only were these new authorities smaller than their predecessors (by somewhere between one-third and half the size), but *much* smaller in terms of lay membership; there were no longer local authority appointees or trade union nominees, though trusts were required to have at least two non-executives resident in the local community. Vestiges of syndicalism remained, however, in the requirement that teaching authorities and trusts had a medical school presence (Department of Health *et al*, 1989, p65) and in the requirement that trust boards should include nursing and medical directors. FHSAs had only a single (chief) executive, together with five lay and four professional non-executives appointed by the RHA (Ham, 1990) and thus maintained something of the fine balance struck by their predecessors. In all, there was a clear move away from any principle of representativeness, a move somewhat emphasised by the decision that trusts need only hold a single public meeting each year (Department of Health, 1989). While the existence and role of CHCs remained (and indeed still remains) controversial in some quarters, they were retained in unchanged form.

The sociological profile of those appointed as chairs and non-executives has been the subject of a great deal of dispute, particularly the extent to which the new authorities were 'packed' with businessmen (sic) and the relatives of prominent Conservatives. It is, however, clear that, as far as trusts were concerned, chairs and non-executives were somewhat less than typical members of the population; Ashburner and Cairncross's (1992) study revealed that more than half had experience as company directors, three-quarters were male, and 98 per cent described themselves as white.

Further changes in the structure of authorities, to take effect in 1996, were announced in late 1993 (NHS Executive, 1993, p8). First, RHAs were, with immediate effect, to be reduced in number and subsequently abolished; in place of these statutory authorities the regional function would be undertaken by branch offices of the Department of Health's NHS Executive. Second, DHAs and FHSAs were to be merged, entailing the end of a mode of managing the family practitioner services (that is, at arm's length from other services) which had existed long before the inception of the NHS itself (Watkin, 1975, p76). Moreover, the powers of CHCs had already been defined more narrowly (Levitt and Wall, 1992, p288). Overall, these changes could be seen as further steps in the transformation of the NHS hierarchy into a narrowly accountable agent of central government, implicitly dependent for its political legitimacy upon the legitimacy of central government itself.

Such an arrangement is at least coherent in terms of addressing the paradox referred to above. Yet there remain considerable discomforts on the part of central government, manifest in continuing appeals to NHS authorities to consult their publics and in numerous initiatives for so doing. (For a review of a number of these, see Coote, 1993.) Indeed, Stephen Dorrell stated that the new merged DHAs/FHSAs:

are responsible for ensuring that local health services respond to local pressures ... [they] will be expected to stimulate public debate in their area and to demonstrate that their plans for the locality respond to public opinion (Dorrell, 1995, p4).

Moreover, concerns about their own political legitimacy have also been expressed on behalf of senior NHS managers by the then president of the Institute of Health Services Management (*Health Service Journal*, 17 June 1993, p13). Whether or not these concerns merely manifest Klein's dictum that governments tend to seek means of centralising the credit for ostensible policy successes and decentralising the blame for more difficult matters (Klein, 1983, p140), it is apparent that the problems of democracy and accountability in the NHS have not yet been solved. But do these problems really matter?

DO ACCOUNTABILITY AND DEMOCRACY MATTER?

The terms 'accountability' and 'democracy' are so widely used rhetorically as terms of approbation that it is sometimes hard to remind ourselves that the concepts that underlie them do need to be defended. For there are arguments against being overly concerned with these issues when faced with many other important problems such as the fragmentation brought about during the last decade of NHS reorganisations (Harrison and Lachmann, 1996). These arguments, which are valid, fall into two broad categories.

The first category of argument points out that the NHS has never, in fact, enjoyed a 'golden age' of democracy and accountability. This is evident from the historical overview presented above. Members of the various statutory health authorities have never been directly elected, except where local government authorities have had NHS responsibilities. Nor have such members ever been sociologically representative of their publics. Indeed, even when efforts were made to give such authorities a broader base by including professionals, trade unionists, local politicians and voluntary workers, such members were always appointed for their *personal* contribution and, however they might have seen themselves, never as formal representatives. And overarching all of this is the disturbing fact that there is little empirical evidence of any substantial influence by such members when compared with that of health professionals and (later) of NHS managers (Harrison, 1988, pp36-7; Harrison *et al*, 1992, pp51-93).

The second category of argument is rather different; it centres upon what might be termed the objections to populism. Popular opinion is likely to be more illiberal than elite opinion, a phenomenon frequently observed in connection with such issues as capital and corporal punishment (Klein, 1974). In the health care field such illiberal attitudes would, to judge from experience in the US state of Oregon, probably be represented in a lack of priority for services for AIDS sufferers or drug/alcohol abusers (see, for instance, Dixon and Welch, 1991). Elsewhere, we have given an account of a debate in Britain about assisted conception for an unmarried couple (Harrison and Hunter, 1994, p40), which supports a similar conclusion.

The validity of the above arguments does not, however, mean that there are not alternative arguments which are sufficient to outweigh them. We believe that there are at present three imperatives for an enhancement of democracy, accountability and consumerism (in the senses set out in our introduction) within the NHS. First, elite behaviour can easily become corrosive of standards in public life, a term that does not relate narrowly to the public sector but includes, for instance, the directorship of public companies. This has been recently demonstrated both within and outside the NHS where the inflated salaries of chief executives of former public utilities, the allegations that members of parliament have asked parliamentary questions in return for payment, and the revelation that large sums of expenditure on information technology had been inappropriately incurred by Regional Health Authorities have shown a need for checks on the pursuit of self-interest by such elites. Greater accountability is required.

Second, it has become evident that the rationing of health care is increasingly explicit and that improved means of legitimating such painful and contentious choices are needed (Harrison and Hunter, 1994). As was shown in our introduction, such legitimacy cannot derive simply from the preferences of users; by extension, it cannot derive from the preferences of health professionals, who are likely to display an intellectual commitment to their specialty that parallels the user's emotional commitment to his/her own problem and its treatment. Greater democracy is required in order to balance the whole of the public interest.

Third, it seems certain that the emphasis given by the present government to 'consumerism' as expressed especially through the *Citizen's Charter* and its offspring, including the *Patients' Charter*, (Department of Health, 1991) will have had an effect on the expectations of users of the NHS. The Service derives much of its public support (Harrison, 1988, pp86-91) from the universality of its provision, and therefore needs to retain as users those who might most readily go elsewhere. There is a need for greater responsiveness to users. In our final section, we set out a number of organisational options for enhancing and balancing these requirements and the other considerations that we have discussed.

OPTIONS FOR THE FUTURE

A key theme of the 1991 NHS changes was the desire to shift the service from being producer-led to being user-driven. However, this was not to be achieved by injecting a greater degree of democracy into the NHS but by using the language and mechanisms of the marketplace, in which the individual consumer exercises his or her preferences by choosing which health care resource to access. The theory was that money would follow the patient once a GP had decided upon a particular course of action in conjunction with each patient. In this way, users' views would be sought, listened to and acted upon. The reality has been quite different with money *preceding* the patient as a consequence of block contracts (the preferred form of contracting) placed by health authorities and covering all categories of care or numbers of particular medical interventions.

Another component of the market philosophy designed to empower users has been the Patients' Charter but this has been criticised for being a muddle and a sham - a gimmick rather than a serious attempt to define enforceable rights for citizens.

If the intention is to achieve greater responsiveness to users through enhanced democracy and/or consumerism then a number of options can be listed within these two categories. The Labour Party health policy statement of 1995 addressed the issue of democracy and reference will be made to it at relevant points in the subsequent discussion (The Labour Party, 1995).

Options for democracy

◆ return to pre-1991 arrangements

◆ elected health authorities

◆ elected chairs with appointed directors

◆ local authorities as health and social services purchasers

◆ non-local solutions, e.g. national accountability and rights/ charter packages.

In practice, these alternative options cannot be separated from future government decisions about local authorities and regional government, or about NHS organisation in general. But major changes in these areas are not expected by either Conservative or Labour governments. Indeed, in its health policy statements, the Labour Party seems intent upon retaining the current system of selected boards at health authority and trust levels although it would ensure that there was a wider representation of local interests on such boards. In particular, it would encourage local authority members, such as chairs of social services committees, to become members of health authorities, but it would not make these changes mandatory. They would remain voluntary.

Options for consumerism

◆ vouchers in primary care
◆ more influential CHCs
◆ improved complaints procedures.

The remainder of this section examines some of the principal strengths and weaknesses of each of these various options.

Return to pre-1991 arrangements
The pre-1991 arrangements centred on health authorities, a proportion of whose members were elected local authority members. The rest were appointed and were agents of the secretary of state for health. Although the local authority members were not directly elected, it was believed that indirect election through local authority membership was more democratic than the alternative of selection. But the arrangement was criticised on the grounds that the local authority members either made health authorities too party political or else they contributed little to the discussions. It was widely believed that such an arrangement offers the worst of both worlds. The health authority was neither democratically elected but nor was it unequivocally an appointed body. Consequently, it was not clear what the status of the local authority members was on the health authority when they had not been directly elected for that purpose.

There is little support for returning to such an arrangement, although the Labour Party proposals for broadening the membership base of trust boards and health authorities come close to that and retain echoes of the old system. Although the Labour Party does not advocate packing health authorities with local authority members it does suggest that chairs of social services committees might be particularly appropriate individuals to have on health authorities and trust boards.

Elected health authorities
The option of elected health authorities has been proposed as an alternative to the continuation of an appointed system of membership on the one hand and the merging of health with local government on the other. It is not clear whether there would be popular support for elected health authorities or what the turn out would be at election time. Certainly, other countries which have experimented with such a model have

not found it to be an overwhelming success. The turnout at such elections has been low, and adding yet another election on top of local government and central government elections could be confusing as well as costly. Therefore, the criteria that should govern the decision about whether directly elected health authorities would be appropriate or not are as follows:

◆ whether a separate election is likely to arouse sufficient interest
◆ the extent to which the responsibilities involved are related to other community services and in particular to those of local authorities.

While the responsibilities of district health authorities could be judged to be more than sufficient to justify a separate election, the interrelationship between health services and other community services has to be taken into account. A separately elected health authority might do nothing to resolve the problem of the division between local authorities' responsibilities and those of health authorities. Indeed, it could even aggravate them by creating another elected authority with its own claim to a mandate and with the possibility of a different form of political control.

Elected Chairs with Appointed Directors

A compromise solution has been proposed whereby health authorities would remain appointed but the chairs would be elected. This would not only provide some democratic input into the running of the health service locally but would also allow the role of chairs to be seen to be quite separate from that of the executive directors. At present the role of chief executives and that of chairs is a very close one - sometimes too close - and the effect can often be to the detriment of the successful working of the health authority as a corporate team in which the non-executive directors feel fully involved. The election of chairs would help to avoid such a collusive and perhaps not altogether healthy relationship. On the other hand, elected chairs could lead to problems over the loyalty that they would feel to their local electorate and the loyalty that the appointed members would feel to those who had appointed them. The chairs and the appointed members would not necessarily be able to agree on priorities or on other matters to do with the running of the authority. Such an option seems to confuse, in a particularly dysfunctional way, the democratic principle of election and the undemocratic principle of selection/appointment.

Local authorities as health and social services purchasers

The main alternative to bringing the health service under local democratic control would be to make the health service the responsibility of local authorities. Various commentators and organisations, such as the Association of Metropolitan Authorities, have proposed various options for local authority control of the health service (AMA, 1994; Harrison *et al*, 1991; Harrison and Hunter, 1994; Clarke, Hunter and Wistow, 1995; Cooper *et al*, 1995). Under these proposals, the district health authority would be the commissioning authority for health within a locality. It is assumed that the local authority would exercise control over its responsibilities for the health service through a committee and departmental structure, although other variations would be possible. In recent years, local authorities have learned different ways of working, using different forms of relationship. Local authorities have developed the use of contracts with external and internal providers, controlling internal direct service organisations through management boards on which officers and councillors may sit together operating outside the constraints of the normal committee system. Local authorities have introduced devolved management, particularly in relation to the local management of schools. Furthermore, local authorities have created various forms of hands-off organisations such as trusts or companies, often in partnership with other agencies.

The model for local government taking over the health service proposed by the AMA follows that adopted in passenger transport in the Metropolitan areas, where the Passenger Transport Authority has a joint board consisting of elected members to determine the budget and policy to be applied by the Passenger Transport Executive composed of managers appointed by the councillors. The proposal for a health and social services commissioning agency follows this model although it would not require a joint board. Such a model could be adopted even if the relationship between the health authority and the operational services were modified as suggested in the Labour Party's 1995 health policy statement. Such a model is probably the minimum required to secure continuing democratic control through local government. It would not need an internal market to justify the separation between purchasing/commissioning activity and the provision of services.

Transfer of responsibilities to a local authority or to a new elected body does not mean that central government relaxes all control over it. In most local government services there are national interests as well as local ones. In most services the balance between the two is achieved by local authorities operating within a framework of legislation, inspection and regulation. Central accountability for that framework can be combined with local accountability for action taken within it and that is what is proposed for the new role of health authorities. At the same time, any policy to extend the responsibilities of local authorities should be accompanied by a process of strengthening local authorities' accountability. This might be achieved through a variety of means such as health panels representing local users of services or citizens' juries whereby members of the public are involved in aspects of priority setting and decision making. But these mechanisms would be supplementary to the principle of direct elections, not a substitute for it.

In principle, the local government scenario offers three important benefits to health policy. First, it provides a direct democratic input. Second, it offers, though does not *guarantee*, full integration of health and social care planning and purchasing, ending the present artificial division between the two, and the perverse incentives this generates. Third, it brings health *treatment* and care into a policy arena which includes other important determinants of health. Environmental health, local roads and traffic, and public housing are all still substantially regulated by local government authorities.

The last two points are relatively uncontentious. More problematic is the core ideal of local democracy. Arguments against local democracy fall into two categories both employed by the National Association of Health Authorities and trusts in its discussion paper of the subject (NAHAT, 1993). The first argument is essentially that local government is not really democratic at all, being both over politicised and over bureaucratised with important decisions being made by councillors and a correspondingly reduced role for managers. This is a contradictory argument: the fact that councillors take decisions (if they do) makes local government more, rather than less, democratic. It also fails to take account of the undemocratic nature of central government which would otherwise continue to control health policy - the British political system provides for the continued dominance of the executive over the legislature and, as Stewart (1992) has argued, democracy consists of little more than periodic general elections.

Over the last fifteen to twenty years, local government has seen its role cut back by central government and its status reduced. The local government option for the health service could breath new life and political salience into local government by giving it powers to take decisions which would be seen locally as important.

Non-local solutions

An alternative to solutions based on some form of local democracy or improvements in the way in which appointed authorities function in a given locality is to adopt at national level a set of explicit health care rights based on equity of process within the limits of an agreed health care package (Coote, 1994). People with specified needs would thus have rights to receive care and/or treatment aimed at meeting those needs. In this option, rights would be statutorily based and therefore quite different from the present Patients' Charter. There are various ways in which such entitlements to health care might be delivered. For some, promoting individual rights, with corresponding responsibilities, helps to set limits upon collective activity. What you don't have a right to, by implication, you don't get. Others see entitlement to social goods as a way of strengthening and deepening democracy. Rights to education and health care are regarded as essential components of citizenship because these things make it possible for individuals to exercise their civil and political rights and more generally to participate in society.

Linked to this notion is the idea that rights help to shift power from planners and providers of social goods to citizens and service users. This suggests a model of social provision built not on paternalism or philanthropy but on the principle of equal citizenship and self-determination. Instead of being at the mercy of politicians and professionals who decide in paternalistic fashion who needs what, individuals should be able to claim what has been designated by prior agreement through the democratic process as theirs by right.

There is a useful distinction to be made between substantive and procedural social rights, and these two kinds of rights can be tackled in different ways and with different funding implications. Substantive rights are rights to actual benefits and services, e.g. to a hospital bed, a course of treatment, an operation and so on. Procedural rights are rights to the fair treatment of individuals as they come into contact with service providers. It is almost certainly easier to predict and control the costs of enforcing fair procedures whereas the introduction of enforceable rights to substantive services and benefits would imply unpredictable and open-ended demands on public funds. It is easier in practical terms to envisage individuals having some enforceable entitlements to be treated in fair terms than that they should have enforceable entitlements to whatever treatment they might require or is available. Procedural rights are based on principles of fairness which are already well established in law. In effect, introducing such rights would mean extending civil liberties to the realm of social provision.

It has been suggested that an alternative to the Patients' Charter might be a health charter in which three kinds of rights would be enshrined (Coote, 1994):

◆ **Aspirational rights**, or aims and values - what ought to be. These would not be expressed as individual enforceable rights but as statements of intent. As such, they would be implemented by means of duties imposed on public authorities expressed by goals and timetables with procedures for review. All of these would be explicit and open so that citizens could follow and assess progress towards stated goals.

◆ **Quality standards** which would address the performance of health service providers and the impact of health services upon the health of the nation as a whole, upon disadvantaged or otherwise vulnerable groups and upon individual health service consumers. These are not individually enforceable rights but rather objectives. Duties can be placed upon health service providers to pursue specific quality standards with timetables and procedures for reviewing progress towards clear objectives backed up by a complaints procedure. This is something the Patients' Charter already sets out to achieve more realistically than its attempt to talk about rights. But what is missing is a framework for quality assurance which clearly establishes the broad purpose for which services are intended. The Patients' Charter is obsessed with competition and choice and has nothing to say about equity. Any attempt to improve standards must improve them for all on an equitable basis. What is also missing is any recognised role for the public in defining standards and measuring and assessing performance. It may be possible to specify procedural rights for citizens to participate in decisions about defining and assessing quality and for such rights to be enforced by the health commissioner or ombudsman when the final appeal goes to court. The important thing is to be clear about what is being promised and what is not, what can be guaranteed as a right to citizens and what cannot.

◆ **Enforceable patients' rights**. These may usefully be based on the principles of procedural fairness. Rights of access to a GP and to emergency services, information about available services and reasons for decisions, informed consent, confidentiality, complaint and appeal procedures are all examples of appropriate procedural rights. The Health Charter would set out clear and effective enforcement procedures to ensure that such rights were effective.

In respect of a more consumerist approach, there are various possibilities. Three are considered here.

Vouchers in primary care

If funds are truly to follow the patient then a voucher system may be more appropriate and successful as an instrument of policy. It is also an attractive solution to those on the political right who wish to restore decision-making power and choice to individuals. Just as the argument about vouchers in schools is now high on the political agenda, it may only be a matter of time, though not this side of a general election, before similar arguments surface in respect of health. The idea already has many advocates. At the time of the NHS review in the late 1980s there were calls for the introduction of a voucher system.

The chief drawback to vouchers is the difficulty in setting them at a meaningful level for individuals while also including an element of risk pooling and community rating. The danger is that the vouchers could be set at too low a level to cover a comprehensive range of health care needs. At the other extreme is the risk of setting the voucher at such a high level that the system would be prohibitively expensive. Another problem with vouchers is the risk of adverse selection which may be triggered. This would apply in respect of elderly people as well as those suffering from chronic conditions. But the particular attraction of vouchers is that they restore to the individual the ability to exercise real choice over which services to utilise. A variant of the voucher scheme has been the Independent Living Fund in respect of disabled people. Now abolished, this fund was particularly attractive because it enabled individuals to exercise their own choices about which services to access.

More effective community health councils

CHCs, somewhat paradoxically, are the remaining vestige of the old NHS and are the only quasi-independent voice in the NHS (Winkler, 1995). Established in 1974 following the first major reorganisation of the NHS, they are the only piece of machinery not to have undergone fundamental reform since then. More recently, questions have been asked about the continuing relevance of CHCs and their future role given the absence of Regional Health Authorities from April 1996, since RHAs have been the principal means by which Councils have retained some element of independence.

CHCs are by no means representative of local consumers. They offer little more than a weak form of an independent watchdog. There are those who believe that, with the development of alternative mechanisms for ensuring the consumer voice such as health panels, citizens juries and forums of other kinds, the role of CHCs will become more and more redundant. Whether such a scenario is likely will depend to a great extent on the success of the alternatives. CHCs seem likely to survive particularly if their role, which is to challenge and on occasion disagree with the management agenda, is understood and accepted.

The Labour Party seeks to strengthen CHCs by turning them into local advocacy services. They would be given real powers to monitor, regulate and inspect local services as well as act as advocates on behalf of local users. They would also be seen as more representative of local communities than is presently the case. Certainly, CHCs seem to be at something of a crossroads. They must either develop into more effective bodies representing local user views or else they will wither away as other initiatives aimed at involving the public take root. But it will be some time before the latter occurs - if at all. The best hope, therefore, lies in making CHCs truly effective. A membership more representative of local communities would be a start. But, as Cooper *et al* (1995, p46) argue,

> what is needed is a fundamental shift in the balance of power so that the reconstituted and reinvigorated CHC can demand NHS senior executives to report to its

meetings rather than the CHC being grateful that it is allowed to attend health authority and trust boards.

Improved complaints procedures

For years complaints procedures in the NHS have been a matter of concern and ridicule. From April 1996 new procedures were introduced following an independent review led by Professor Alan Wilson, Vice-Chancellor of Leeds University (Department of Health, 1994). The changes are designed to make the system simpler and quicker and are a response to the growing number of complaints prompted by the Patients' Charter and a more rights-conscious public. The new procedures do not preclude resort to the Ombudsman in the event of any dissatisfaction with the response from the NHS. CHCs will also continue to offer advice and support to complainants.

Traditionally complaints have been viewed negatively as criticisms of individuals or services and as a sign of falling standards. They tended not to be taken seriously. But, as the former assistant director of the Consumers' Association has argued, 'complaints have an absolutely fundamental role in the delivery of health care. They are the most positive and wonderful thing any service can get their hands on'. The new orthodoxy takes the view that complaints are to be treasured with the rising number of complaints to be regarded as a sign of progress (Cole, 1995). It demonstrates the growth of a new consumer consciousness which is welcome and overdue. Whereas people would rarely complain after waiting for several hours to be seen in out-patients now they will complain after waiting for more than half-an-hour. Such feedback is essential in raising standards, improving services and exposing weakness in the organisation and management of care.

A simpler, speedier complaints system should encourage people to use it, especially if the complaints are dealt with in the context of an overall management ethos which sets great store by receiving and acting on criticism. Most complaints occur as a result of breakdowns in communication and in rude uncaring attitudes on the part of staff. These problems can be handled relatively easily unless they are indicative of deeper flaws. As the Wilson report stresses, there is no point in encouraging complaints if the resources do not exist to make the improvements which may be required.

ASSESSMENT

As we noted earlier, the need to legitimise difficult decisions is likely to become a more important feature of the NHS unless there is a major injection of new money, which seems unlikely under any future government. As we showed in the introduction, such legitimacy cannot be derived simply from the preferences of users; nor can it derive from the preferences of health professionals. Greater democracy is required in order to provide some sort of public interest, input and balance. In this last section we have reviewed a range of mechanisms which have been put forward at various times by various analysts and commentators, all seeking in different ways to provide for greater user influence over health care decisions. The real debate is over whether there is an attempt to move towards greater democratic control over health authorities or whether the system of appointment remains largely intact with the user voice being strengthened in other ways which owe their origins to consumerist developments like the Patients' Charter.

In seeking solutions to the 'democratic deficit' in the NHS, to which many observers have drawn attention, the central issue is to find ways of balancing the needs of the individual with the needs of the wider community. Whereas options for consumerism are concerned with the needs of the individual, options focusing on democratic changes are directed towards meeting the needs of the community as a whole. There is no reason why any reforming government should pursue one option rather than the other. A combination of democratic and consumerist solutions is quite possible. Moreover, it is also possible to combine various democratic options. For example, one such combination would involve nationally determined statutory rights to individual health care enforceable by local government authorities who would be responsible for purchasing not only services to meet specific health care entitlements but also services to meet other locally determined non-statutory priorities.

It would appear that no one option on its own is fully capable of addressing both the democratic and the consumerist issues that are alive in health policy. Some combination of the two, therefore, would seem to offer the optimal way forward. However, in seeking to find an appropriate balance between the two approaches it will be necessary to acknowledge the inevitability of a degree of tension between meeting individual aspirations on the one hand and those of the community, i.e. the collective, on the other. At present, the position is wholly unbalanced with an undue focus on individual rights and a lack of effective democratic representation for the collective. No political party seems to favour reforming local government in such a way as to enable health to be brought within its embrace. Yet, as we have argued, this offers the best way forward in terms of addressing the absence of democracy which is currently a feature of the NHS.

References

Ashburner L. and Cairncross L., 'Membership of the 'new style' health authorities: continuity or change?', *Public Administration*, Vol. 71, No. 3, 1993, pp357-75.

Association of Metropolitan Authorities, *The Future Role of Local Authorities in the Provision of Health Services*, AMA, London 1994.

Castle B., *The Castle Diaries 1974-76*, Weidenfeld and Nicholson, London 1980.

Clarke M., Hunter D. J. and Wistow G., *The NHS and Local government: The New Agenda*, Local Government Management Board, Luton 1995.

Cole A., 'Should Complaints be Treasured?', *Health Service Journal*, 28 September 1995, pp24-27.

Committee of Enquiry into the Cost of the National Health Service, (Chairman: Mr C.W. Guillebaud), *Report*, Cmnd 663, HMSO, London 1956.

Cooper L., Coote A., Davies A. and Jackson C., *Voices Off: tackling the democratic deficit in health*, London: Institute for Public Policy Research, 1995..

Coote A., 'Public participation in decisions about health care', *Critical Public Health*, Vol. 4, No. 1, 1993, pp36-48.

Coote A., *Equity and Health: The role of rights*, unpublished preliminary notes prepared for forthcoming IPPR report on Citizens' Charter, 1994.

Day P. and Klein R.E., *Accountabilities: Five Public Services*, Tavistock, London 1987.

Department of Health, *Self-Governing Hospitals: an initial guide*, HMSO, London 1989.

Department of Health, *The Patients' Charter*, London 1991.

Department of Health, *Being Heard*, The Report of a Review Committee on NHS Complaints Procedures, DoH, London 1994.

Department of Health and Social Security, *The Future Structure of the National Health Service*, (The Crossman Green Paper), HMSO, London 1970.

Department of Health and Social Security, *Democracy in the National Health Service*, HMSO, London 1974.

Department of Health, Welsh Office, Scottish Home and Health Department, and Northern Ireland Office, *Working for Patients*, Cm 555, HMSO, London 1989.

Dixon J. and Welch H.G., 'Priority Setting: Lessons from Oregon', *The Lancet*, Vol. 337, 13 April 1991, pp891-4.

Dorrell S., 'Health the new agenda', Speech, 29 July 1995.

Foote M., *Aneurin Bevan 1945-1960*, Paladin, London 1973.

Greene A., *Medical Care System Financed by Savings and Catastrophic Insurance*, Mimeo: paper prepared for Healthcare 2000, 1995.

Hallas J., *CHCs in Action*, Nuffield Provincial Hospitals Trust, London 1976.

Ham C.J., 'Community Health Council Participation in the NHS Planning System', *Social Policy and Administration*, Vol. 14, No. 3, 1980, pp221-231.

Ham C.J., *The Governance of Health Services*, Community Services Topic Paper no. 1.8, University of Birmingham Department of Social Administration, Birmingham 1985.

Ham C.J., *Holding on While Letting Go: A report on the relationship between directly managed units and DHAs*, King's Fund College, London 1990.

Harrison S., *Managing the National Health Service: shifting the frontier?*, Chapman and Hall, London 1988.

Harrison S., 'Clinical autonomy and planned markets: the British Case' in R.B. Saltman and C. von Otter (eds), *Implementing Planned Markets in Health Care: Balancing Social and Economic Responsibility*, Open University Press, Buckingham 1995.

Harrison S. and Hunter D.J., *Rationing Health Care*, Institute for Public Policy Research, London 1994.

Harrison S., Hunter D. J., Johnston I. H., Nicholson N., Thunhurst C. and Wistow G., *Health Before Health Care*, Social Policy Paper No. 4, Institute for Public Policy Research, London 1991.

Harrison S., Hunter D.J., Marnoch G. and Pollitt C.J., *Just Managing: power and culture in the National Health Service*, Macmillan, London 1992.

Harrison S., Hunter D.J. and Pollitt C., *The Dynamics of British Health Policy*, Unwin Hyman, London 1990.

Harrison S. and Lachmann P.J., *Towards a high-trust NHS: proposals for minimally invasive reforms*, Institute for Public Policy Research, London 1996.

Harrison S. and Wistow G., 'The purchaser/provider split in English health care: towards explicit rationing?', *Policy and Politics*, Vol. 20, No. 2, 1992, pp123-30.

Jowell R., Witherspoon S. and Brook L., *British Social Attitudes: special international report*, Gower, Aldershot 1991.

Klein R.E., 'The Case for Elitism: Public Opinion and Public Policy', *Political Quarterly*, Vol. 45, No. 4, 1974, pp406-417.

Klein R.E., *The Politics of the National Health Service*, Longman, London 1983.

Klein R.E. and Lewis J., *The Politics of Consumer Representation*, Centre for Studies in Social Policy, London 1976.

Lee K. and Mills A., *Policy-Making and Planning in the Health Sector*, Croom Helm, London 1982.

Levitt R., *The Reorganised National Health Service*, 2nd edition, Croom Helm, London 1979.

Levitt R. and Wall A., *The Reorganised National Health Service*, Croom Helm, London 1984.

Levitt R., Wall A. and Appleby J., *The Reorganised National Health Service*, (fifth edition), Chapman and Hall, London 1995.

National Association of Health Authorities and Trusts, *Securing Effective Public Accountability in the NHS: A Discussion Paper*, NAHAT, Birmingham 1993.

NHS Executive, *Managing the New NHS: functions and responsibilities in the new NHS*, Department of Health, London 1993.

Pollitt C. and Harrison S. (eds), *The Handbook of Public Services Management*, Blackwell, Oxford 1992.

Pressman J.L. and Wildavsky A., *Implementation: How Great Expectations in Washington are Dashed in Oakland*, University of California Press, Berkeley, Ca. 1979.

Roche M., *Rethinking Citizenship: welfare, ideology and change in modern society*, Polity Press, Cambridge 1992.

Royal Commission on Local government, (Chairman: Lord Radcliffe-Mand), *Report*, Cmnd 4040, HMSO, London 1969.

Royal Commission on the National Health Service, (Chairman: Sir Alec Merrison), *Report*, Cmnd 7615, HMSO, London 1979.

Schulz R.I. and Harrison S., *Teams and Top Managers in the NHS: a Survey and a Strategy*, King's Fund Project Paper no. 41, London 1983.

Stewart J., *Accountability to the Public*, European Policy Forum, London 1992.

The Labour Party, *Renewing the NHS: Labour's Agenda for a Healthier Britain*, Labour Party, London 1995.

Webster C., *The Health Services Since the War: Volume I: problems of health care - the National Health Service before 1957*, HMSO, London 1988.

Willcocks A.J., *The Creation of the National Health Service*, Routledge and Kegan Paul, London 1967.

Winkler F., 'Consumer Groups' in Merry P. (ed), *1995/96 Annual NHS Handbook*, (Tenth Edition), NAHAT, Birmingham 1995.

RATIONING IN THE
'REFORMED' NHS

Allyson M Pollock

Health care is often viewed in economic terms as a merit good, that is, as being both essential and desirable for society. But health care is an emotive subject: it is highly politicised, demand and need often appear to outstrip resources, and the individuals requiring services (patients) are often vulnerable and visible. To make things more complicated, at the patient doctor interface the distributor of scarce resources (doctor) has a large degree of freedom over how resources are distributed for individual patients. These conditions are a recipe for conflict - between society and the individual patient, between state and doctor.

This conflict is not new. Throughout the history of the NHS there have been insufficient resources to meet demands or needs. Therefore rationing - withholding potentially beneficial treatments from individual patients or groups of patients - has been inevitable. Rationing implies equal and fair share, this is the basis of the health care delivery in the NHS, where equity, and not ability to pay determines access to care.

It is well known that the NHS has not always achieved its objective of equity and fairness. The proponents of the implementation of the NHS and Community Care Act 1991 claim that the process of resource allocation in the NHS is now more visible and that rationing is more explicit (Klein, 1991). The question still remains, is it fair? This chapter considers these two issues asking the reader first to decide whether the internal market has made rationing more explicit and then to consider whether the mechanisms for distributing resources and services within the 1991 NHS are fair.

1. HOW RESOURCES ARE ALLOCATED AT DIFFERENT LEVELS OF THE INTERNAL MARKET WITHIN THE NHS.

Overall spending on health

The ability of the UK to contain health care spending through a global budget and to provide comprehensive universal coverage has been impressive, and many countries have attempted to follow suit (Critical Public Health, 1993). Both the absolute level of expenditure on health care in the UK (including private health care) at around 6 per cent of GDP and the rate of increase is considerably lower than most other OECD countries.

Compared to other areas of public spending, the NHS has done well. Over the past ten years real expenditure rose on average by 3 per cent annually even when real government expenditure fell in the mid to late 1980s. But this increase fell short of the official Department of Health estimates of the resources required to keep pace with need, the effect of ageing, new technologies and recommended wage increases. In 1988 the Select Committee on Health estimated that the NHS had been underfunded by around half a per cent of total costs per year through out the 1980s (Social Services Committee, 1988).

Allocations to regions, districts and fundholders

The key to any debate on rationing or priority setting is not just whether overall levels of spending are adequate but also whether the current mechanisms for distributing resources are fair. Unlike the US where rationing is based on ability to pay, one of the triumphs of the NHS has been the ability to distribute resources on the basis of health care needs. The NHS has striven to overcome the enormous inequities in provision inherited in 1948 in a number of ways, for example: by controlling the distribution of GPs, by regulating controls on the distribution and expansion of hospitals and beds through the hospital plan of the 1960s, by establishing controls on medical and paramedical staffing, and in the 1970s introducing a national resource allocation formula (RAWP) which made the mechanism for allocating central funds to the regions explicit (Klein, 1983).

In 1991 a new funding formula replaced RAWP. Resources were allocated to regions as per head of population payments (capitation payments). This allocation included weighting factors, such as age and the standardised mortality ratio which allow for the higher needs and costs of young children and older people. Different regions developed different formulae to allocate resources to districts, but it is not known how equitable these formulae were. However, in general the formulae favoured populations with large numbers of healthy elderly people and work, against areas with young populations with high rates of morbidity and mortality (Rafferty, 1993). The result was a transfer of resources away from the north of the country and from most deprived inner city areas towards the south east of England. In many inner city areas up to 25 per cent of the projected five year budget may have been lost as a result. The national funding formulae have again been revised for 1997 (Smith, Sheldon, Carr-Hill *et al*, 1994).

GP fundholder allocations

GP fundholding was introduced in April 1991 along with the other NHS reforms. GP fundholding is a voluntary scheme where GPs use resources allocated out of the health authority budget to purchase some hospital and community services for their patients. More funds for GP fundholders means less for the parent health authority - and vice versa. Unlike the district health authorities, GP fundholders are not yet funded on a per capita basis but on the historical use of services by their patients. It has been difficult to develop a capitation formula for fundholders (Smith, Sheldon, Carr-Hill *et al*,1994) but the current method of historical funding is likely to lead to inequities between fundholding and non-fundholding practices (Dixon, 1994).

Although a national committee was set up to review fundholding allocations, attempts to derive a fair formula for fundholders have been unsuccessful to date. It is unclear whether it will be possible to develop a robust formula in future for practice-sized populations.

Expenditure by districts and GP fundholders

Overall resource allocation by the Treasury to the NHS, to regional health authorities (RHAs) and to district health authorities (DHAs) is essentially the same as it was in the pre-1991 NHS. The difference lies in the way resources are allocated by DHAs and GP fundholders.

Prior to 1991, district health authorities were responsible for purchasing and providing hospital and community health services within their geographic boundaries. Resources were allocated to hospitals and providers of community health services more or less as they were spent. When funds ran low at the end of the year, hospital wards were closed and patients simply waited longer on waiting lists, or health authorities would negotiate with regions for contingency funds.

In 1991, the NHS and Community Care Act (1990) separated the purchasing and providing function of health authorities and introduced GP fundholding. Health authorities are responsible for assessing the health needs of their resident populations and setting contracts for hospital care and community health care to reflect these.

The internal market has had an important effect on rationing. Now DHAs and GP fundholders must indicate in advance, on the basis of contracts with providers, which services to buy, how much of them and where. This has led to claims by politicians and policymakers that decisions on how resources are spent will be more visible, more accountable and open to public scrutiny.

Allocating resources more explicitly?

Klein has pointed out that there are several layers of decision-making within the NHS which conceal how and where decisions are made about priorities (Klein, 1992). He identifies two levels of priority setting: the macro level, where financial decisions predominate (how resources are allocated to regions, district purchasers and GP fundholders) and a micro level where decisions are made on a clinical basis for individual patients. Klein notes that, 'it is not yet self evident that there is adequate information about how broad macro decisions about priorities taken at the top of the hierarchy translate into clinical decisions at the bottom about who should be treated and how'. But conversely, clinical decisions also influence national and local priorities. Clinical decisions can be translated into interventions and aggregated into population measures of need for services, which - together with available evidence on health care needs, effectiveness and outcomes - can shape the basis for priority setting at national and local level.

Are contracts an explicit rationing tool?

DHAs set out in their annual purchasing intentions or purchasing plans a broad overview of how they intend to allocate their resources for the following year. These plans usually do not detail service contracts nor the level of service that providers are expected to deliver to local residents annually. This information is contained in detailed service specifications or contracts which are drawn up with individual providers by purchasers.

Contracts are set annually on the basis of prospective payments. There are three types of contract. The first of these is the 'block' contract where health authorities would pay a fixed amount of money to providers who would in turn treat all patients referred. Block contracts are usually based on a specialty or client group, for example geriatric services or mental health services, where the providers are required to provide a spectrum of integrated treatment and care. These still comprise around 80 per cent of all contracts. Subsumed within or existing independently of block contracts are 'cost and volume' contracts, in which the purchaser will specify the amount of activity the provider is expected to undertake. For example, a surgical contract may include several cost and volume contracts stipulating the number of cases to be treated by diagnosis and surgical procedure, although for the majority of surgical conditions operations are not separated out. This is the type of contract most commonly used by GPs. Finally there is the 'cost per case' contract (NAHAT, 1993: DoH survey of purchasing) which normally relates to expensive procedures such as heart transplants or expensive rare diseases and conditions.

In addition to these contracts, which are set annually, there are two other ad hoc types of contract: the extracontractual referral and the special contractual placement. These are the most visible of the rationing tools. In the extracontractual referral the purchaser has no contract with a provider and authorisation has to be given prior to treatment. This type of contract focuses on the individual patient and their access to treatment. For example, in 1995 in the case of 'Child B' in Cambridgeshire, judges upheld the decision by doctors and the local health authority to deny treatment to a child with an unusual cancer. The parents had argued that the health authority should pay for care in a private hospital which was prepared to offer treatment. The child was found a place funded by a private individual until her death in May 1996.

The special contractual placement is a cost per case contract, but in this case agreement has to be reached between two or more funding agencies, usually health and social services, over the long-term or continuing care needs of a patient. The contract for the placement usually refers to individuals with special needs, and the decision has to be made about eligibility for services and funding sources. The conflict in this type of decision is two-fold. The process can result in authorities denying responsibility for care and in cost shunting, either to health or to social services, in which case the individual risks passing from a free service to one that is means tested. In the majority of special contractual referrals it is very hard to distinguish between what is health and what is social care. For example, does the woman who is left paraplegic after a stroke, in a vegetative state with a gastrostomy need health or social care, similarly, what of the young man rendered quadriplegic after an accident?

To date, public and media attention has been drawn to contracts which deny the individual care, but it is possible that, as more block contracts include cost and volume elements, the amount and type of care that a health authority purchases should become more visible, and more open to debate. However, for this to happen health authorities must be able to estimate need for services against the contracted volume, and the uptake and access to services against the needs of different groups within the population. Only then can the public judge whether the basis for contracting and also rationing is correct. However, neither purchasing plans nor public health reports provide any evidence that such detailed analysis has been undertaken, except with respect to a very few disease areas and conditions.

One of the problems is that the contract is derived from past measures of use, which usually reflects a historical pattern of supply and thus may already incorporate a degree of rationing. One way round this is to undertake area-based comparisons of different populations and their experience of disease and interventions and outcomes within and across health districts. In recent years elegant work has been undertaken in both coronary heart disease and colorectal cancer to demonstrate how certain groups, including women, ethnic minorities and those of lower socio-economic status, are discriminated against when interventions are compared against needs and outcomes. However, these analyses identify groups which may be discriminated against and not the individuals themselves or the basis for discrimination or rationing. Moreover, these analyses are confined only to those areas where data exists, usually surgical interventions and acute hospital care. For the vast majority of care it is very difficult to link measures of need to service provision and uptake.

DHAs have been unwilling to curtail services completely. Reviewing 60 district health authority purchasing plans, Redmayne and Klein found a great deal of pragmatism and 'muddling through' both in districts set to lose and in those set to gain from the capitation formula. They found very few authorities were excluding treatment conditions or groups of patients from care (NAHAT, 1993). However, now there is evidence that DHAs have begun to do so - typically in services dealing with IVF, varicose veins, wisdom teeth, tattoos, gender reassignment surgery etc., although these decisions appear to have been based on emotive rather than clinical or economic reasoning in some districts.

Making rationing more explicit
The contentious and emotive nature of curtailing services or denying individual patients, means that there have been a number of elaborate attempts, since the reforms were introduced, to make purchasing decisions by health authorities appear more democratic, accountable and based on evidence of the effectiveness of treatments. Two of these initiatives are discussed below.

(i) Involving the public: consumerism versus accountability
It has always been recognised that the NHS should be accountable to the people it serves for the public monies it spends (Webster (ed), 1991). The pre-1991 NHS structures made all local providers directly accountable to the health authority holding the budget for the population within their geographic area. In addition health authorities had consumer representation, CHC members and a locally elected local authority member and a union representative. The effect of the 1991 NHS and Community Care Act was to break with the direct accountability of local providers to their local populations through the DHA (Pollock, 1995). DHA membership has been streamlined to exclude local representatives and union members. Hospital and community service providers are no longer directly accountable to DHAs. Most hospital and community services are now provided by self-governing NHS Trusts accountable directly to the Secretary of State for Health through the new regional tiers rather than to their local communities. Trusts earn their income by winning contracts placed by DHAs and GP fundholders. They determine their own management structures as well as the pay and conditions of service for many of the staff they employ. They are responsible for fulfilling their contracts with purchasers and their aim is *to manage their trust effectively and to make a return on their capital stock*. The break with accountability of providers to the DHA makes it difficult for the local public to know where to turn to when things go wrong or when services are not provided or are closed.

The NHS Management Executive has urged purchasers

(health authorities and GP fundholders) to consult the public about its views on health care provision (NHSME, 1992). This purchasers are anxious to do, and a number of initiatives have taken place, such as 'Listening to Local Voices'. The two main approaches are to include patients in drawing up service specifications for contracts, and to involve the public in priority-setting exercises. The scientific and ethical basis of these exercises is seldom examined and yet tens of thousands of pounds have been spent in this way, with little evidence of any improvment in the process of planning and providing services. This is partly because the methodologies have been shown to be so poor as to make the results of the surveys uninterpretable and of little value either to the public or to local decision makers (Pfeffer and Pollock, 1993(a) and 1993(b).

Consumerism has become a poor substitute for accountability. This is analogous to market based systems of health care in the US where the local community has no ability to influence their providers. In the US most providers are part of large chains and companies, they may not be organised on a geographic basis and do not serve local populations; second, providers rate profit for shareholders more highly than patient care; third, local boards do not include local representatives except in the capacity of business people; and fourth, the meetings and business accounts are not open to the public. All of these are rapidly becoming features of the new NHS provider.

(ii) Evidence of effectiveness

The last administration wished to focus on eliminating inefficiencies in clinical systems by requiring purchasing only for those conditions where there is evidence of effectiveness (Pollock, 1992). Interestingly, this particular policy conflicts with other policies. For example, waiting lists were a specific government performance measure; when they continued their rise the government committed many millions of pounds to clearing them regardless of need, priority or effectiveness (Pollock, 1993).

The emphasis on effectiveness can also be used to

illustrate the tensions between benefits to the population and benefits to the individual, and the trade-off between cure and care services.

The rationing paradox: the clinical guideline

It is, of course, possible to devise guidelines which can be used to ration care on the basis of effectiveness. For instance, some guidelines rate access to care on the basis of a clinical score. These assessments more often than not include some value-laden criteria such as age or even gender. Sometimes the logic behind these criteria appears rational, for instance where age is used as a pointer to the likelihood of survival for that individual.

But the problem is more complex. To take the example of coronary heart disease, the incidence of this is highest in older people and trials of active treatment such as thrombolysis show that benefits do accrue both for individuals and for the whole population (ISIS-2 Collaborative Group, 1988). Thus, while the risk of death in a 70 year old individual with a myocardial infarction following intervention is four times that of a person aged less than 60 years, the paradox is that the greatest benefits from treatment will accrue in the older group because this is where the greatest burden of disease lies. Statistics show that 55 more lives per thousand will be saved among people aged over 70 years than among those under 60 years. And yet, up to two thirds of ICUs and CCUs have age-related admission and treatment policies where the age cut-off can be as low as 55 years (Dudley and Burns, 1992). Clinical decisions focus on individuals rather than groups and so the benefits for the population may be discounted or not realised. This could be termed the 'rationing paradox', whereby the process of excluding individuals from care may actually bring about decreased benefits for the population (Pollock, 1995). And, of course, what follows from the above is that for many conditions, treatments and groups of people more resources will be required to treat more people for a given benefit. Clinical guidelines rarely take into account the population benefits of treatment.

Scoring and rating systems commonly conceal value-laden

judgements. A good example is a decision to exclude candidates for liver transplant if they have alcoholic liver disease. The deserving and the undeserving sick - whether these are defined as smokers, sexually promiscuous, alcoholics, the obese or the disabled - may all find the values of the health care professional or certain sections of society operating for or against them, either directly or in clinical guidelines or in treatment scores.

One corollary of this is that specialty areas where guidelines are less easy to quantify in terms of diagnostic investigation and high technology procedures may lose out, e.g. care of the elderly, rehabilitation, pain relief, the treatment of the chronically sick and disabled. Many chronic conditions and rehabilitative services have not been evaluated either because there is no cure or the outcome measures are too crude to measure progress. This phenomenon is illustrated by the fact that the lion's share of audit monies have been directed into the acute side but little has gone into community audit programmes.

Rationing using eligibility criteria for social and nursing home care

In community care, the assessment and care management process is the rationing mechanism. The assessment of need is supposedly the cornerstone of the NHS and Community Care Act, which in 1991 devolved the funding and responsibility for long term-care to local authorities. In theory, the individual decides which services and care they require. The practice is rather different. Because social care funding is not ring-fenced, there are very different levels of service provision across local authority boundaries. The government recognised early on that this would be the case and recommended to local authorities that they develop eligibility criteria to determine who would get services (Dept. of Health, 1990). Funding and rationing decisions are devolved down to local social services. Social care needs are not to be decided by the individual after all but on the basis of eligibility criteria. In each local authority the client now faces three hurdles.

They must first show that they fulfil the eligibility criteria in order to be assessed for services. If they get through to the assessment phase they must then show that their needs fulfil local eligibility criteria for services. And finally they are subject to charging or means-testing for those services.

Eligibility criteria do not reflect need for care but rather the different levels of resources available within local authorities. However, there is no consensus across local authorities as to how to interpret or even to define eligibility. What is happening is that historical levels of provision and historical patterns of resources will determine eligibility for services thus perpetuating historical inequities. Moreover, because eligibility criteria and needs are neither standardised nor explicit, it is difficult for the public to judge whether rationing is being implemented fairly across or within authorities.

2. ARE RATIONING MECHANISMS FAIR?

So far this chapter has focused on whether the market-based system has made decision-making more explicit. It has shown that for the vast majority of health services expenditure there is little evidence of this. This is because the information on which contracting decisions and service decisions are made is often not available, and when it is it is often far from clear how to interpret it. In the next section we try to address whether the market maximises the use of scarce resources and allocates them fairly and efficiently.

i) Is resource allocation fair in the internal market?
Both GP fundholders and the purchasing health authority are now competing for patients and the ability to pool financial risk by having large numbers of patients. District health authorities have achieved this by merging, and GP fundholders are coming together in consortia. There are still no satisfactory formulae for allocating resources to GPs and for the most part many fundholders have been reimbursed not on capitation payments but on the basis of historical activity. It has been estimated that in the former

North West Thames region (population 3.5 million), GP fundholders received between 13 per cent and 40 per cent more per capita for their patients than the health authority for equivalent fundholding type activities (Dixon, Dinwoodie, Hudson *et al*, 1994). In this region in 1993/94, GPs not only cleared their waiting lists and bought in extra services and fundholding clinics but also made £9.3 million savings overall, and £7.5 million savings on the hospital budget. Similar pictures emerge all over the country. In 1993/94, 75 per cent of funds were underspent, totalling £64 million, or 3.5 per cent of total spending. These resources are not available to the parent health authority to purchase health care for all the population. In many districts, money has run out within the financial year and has resulted in lists for elective surgeries being closed to non-fundholding patients. It is clear that there is inequitable funding due to difficulty in deciding on a formula (Sheldon, 1994; Dixon, 1994).

ii) Is the market more efficient ?
That is, is there now more money for patient care?

Efficiency has been one of the hallmarks of NHS administration. Lack of financial administration has meant that administrative costs have been low. However, there are signs that resources are being squandered on administration of the internal market and contracts which have little relevance to patients needs and patient care. One of the greatest inefficiencies has involved the splitting of purchasing authorities and tiny providers. Purchasing authorities are now merging to cover large geographic areas and populations but with a loss of local population focus. Providers, however, have high transaction costs: each provider may have many hundreds of contracts with several purchasers.

The advent of GP fundholding, however, has decreased the efficiencies which might have been gained from the merging of large authorities. For example, with GP fundholders now purchasing care in addition to around 140 district health authorities, there are many thousands of potential GP purchasers, each of whom has the potential to generate hundreds of thousands of contracts with different providers. All contracts require quarterly monitoring and review meetings with each provider. In addition, GP fundholders have to meet with the DHA and local authorities to agree on eligibility criteria for services. Since GP fundholder populations are not coterminous with DHA and LA populations this may involve negotations with several LAs and DHAs. The growth in the management both of district health authorities and GP fundholding practices, at a time when other staffing levels remain static or are decreasing, is one of the few available indicators of the costs of implementation (Beecham, 1994). In the market, more money is being deployed in administration, leaving less for patient-centred care.

iii) Are services being allocated fairly?

Resources are not being allocated fairly. A further concern is the loss of a stable population through which to monitor access to services. Health authorities no longer serve all their residents in their geographic area. Instead, within each geographic area there may be several purchasers acting on behalf of individual residents each placing contracts with different providers. Service needs, service use, and access and outcomes may be difficult to measure or to interpret: first because of the loss of a stable population; second because of small numbers; third because of selection bias with some purchasers recruiting fitter patients; and finally, because it may not be clear which services were the responsibility of which purchaser to buy in and provide.

There is evidence of a two tier system emerging for services. National surveys repeatedly show that providers are being asked, as a condition of contracts or otherwise to give preference to fundholding patients and extra-contractual referrals (President of the Royal Society of Obstetricians and Gynaecologists, 1994). The Royal College of Surgeons Survey revealed that 62 per cent of surgeons had been told to stop or reduce activity and that 33 per cent had been told to give priority to fundholders patients (regardless of clinical priorities) and to extra-contractual referrals (Royal College of Surgeons of England, 1994). Thus the new system has created incentives for a two tier fast track system (Beecham, 1994).

Prior to 1991, all the facilities in a hospital or community unit were available to patients on the basis of need. Now clinical staff are being asked to ration not on the basis of their clinical judgements and need but on the basis of what the purchaser has paid for. Thus the situation can arise where patients with similar needs in neighbouring beds will receive different services. Ability to pay and not need will determine who gets services.

Finally, there is evidence emerging of some purchaser GP fundholders excluding certain categories from their list, and leaving them as the responsibility of non fundholding GPs. On the other hand, some hospitals and community trusts in prosperous areas have benefitted, both from the more favourable funding of their health authorities and fundholders, and from opportunities to increase their income by developing the private health care sector. Their profits are at the expense of those going broke - new winners and losers are emerging (Association of Community Health Councils for England and Wales, 1994).

iv) *Does the market maintain quality?*
Prior to 1991, overspends were used to lever more resources from the Treasury. Since then, the fear of losing contracts has meant that some providers resort to less explicit tactics to deal with threatened overspends. The two methods open to providers are: efficiency savings and income generation. All providers were required to make efficiency savings of around 1.5 to 2.5 per cent per year that is, that they do more for less. Throughout the 1970s and 1980s, efficiency savings were achieved relatively easily, first by selling off assets such as staff accommodation and hospital sites, then by privatising ancillary, catering and laundry services. But since the 1980s, even though the UK Audit Commission drew attention to the fact that efficiency savings could not be expected to

continue, the government continued to demand savings of around 1 to 3 per cent per year on contracts. How these savings have been achieved and their effect on patient care has never been monitored or evaluated.

Measures to reduce the number of beds available and to close theatres and wards (Pollock and Majeed, 1993) have been accompanied by staff reductions and the introduction of changes in skill mix (where posts are often downgraded). Small savings can also be generated by levying car park charges for staff, not employing locum cover, and not providing study leave or paying for further training of nurses and doctors. But costs are only being transferred to staff. Patients and carers are also absorbing many costs, through faster turnover and decreased length of stay, or increasing use of the private sector, all of which displace costs onto individuals and depress standards and quality. Community care, too, has displaced many costs to certain groups of patients and carers (see below).

Alternatively, providers manipulate activity measures in order to appear to be doing more than they are, for example, double counting admissions under different specialties (Clarke and McKee, 1992), or selecting the fitter, less costly patients, which makes them (and the reforms) look more efficient.

v) Capping the budget in a market-based system
When health budgets are capped and every efficiency saving has been made there are only three alternatives: unmet need will grow, providers must find new ways of increasing their income, or purchasers and providers must redefine their responsibilities for funding treatment and care.

a) supplier led demand
Providers can only optimise their access to the pool of limited resources through contracts or by diversifying into treatments which might attract additional sources of revenue. Constraints on spending have been accompanied by the recognition that some types of health care are more lucrative, in other words, a greater focus on the potential for income generation. Thus many providers are changing bed use from NHS to private

pay-bed use and at the same time diversifying into more profitable activities, that is, cherry picking: selecting out low-risk patients, and developing services for the private sector or fundholders in order to remain viable. At the same time there is anecdotal evidence emerging of supplier restrictions on demand, where access to certain treatments for certain groups is discouraged.

b) patient charges

Patient charges were introduced relatively early in the history of the NHS and now account for more than 4 per cent of the total NHS budget. Prescription charges exempt the most vulnerable patient groups - the elderly, children and the poor and chronically sick - from contributions. When eye and dental charges were introduced, fewer people were exempt from charges, including many elderly. The impact of charges is now beginning to show, with decreased access and uptake of dental service in certain areas and a growing polarisation in dental health between the social classes (OCPS, 1993).

But the real growth area is in hidden charges where providers are operating a mixture of public and private charges. Thus tests, investigations, even some treatments and prescriptions, may be offered in a public NHS setting provided the patient pays. There is no standardisation of these policies and payment schedules nor of their impact on different subgroups within the population and their access to treatment and care.

c) redefining treatment and care and health and social care boundaries

The third way to manage the budget is to redefine the areas of territorial responsibility. The NHS is in the process of redefining health with the emphasis on cure and away from care (Carpenter, 1994). The internal market has given extra impetus to this move, especially now that many authorities face real budget cuts. The impact of the internal market on social care provision must also be understood. As purchasers budgets shrink and providers are forced to contract or close, the pressure on NHS acute beds grows. The response to this has been an explicit policy of shifting as much acute care provision as possible into the community. This has been supported in many areas by the top-slicing of primary development monies to foster care in community settings. Although there is no evidence that services will be more appropriately provided or more cost-effective, some services are increasingly being provided in primary health care settings with consultant input, through hospital at home schemes, or even redefined as social service responsibility.

The implications for local authorities and social services are serious. Local authorities are increasingly concerned that the NHS is now substituting those elements of acute care it once provided free in hospital, with care increasingly paid for in and by the community. Hospital at home schemes, rapid discharge, and decreased length of stay schemes which appear to be progressive community care developments are examples of the imperatives to reduce the costs of NHS acute care. Substituting acute care with care in the community leaves the way open for the delineation of health and social care components and thereby the introduction of charging arrangements. But there are other initiatives that have a sting in the tail. The move towards greater joint commissioning between health and local authorities has been hailed as evidence of greater collaboration between the sectors. But is this a double edged sword? In joint commissioning contracts just how will health and social services be defined and who will pay? There are concerns that joint commissioning will simply result in the NHS buying in services which were once free within the NHS thus transferring them into a means-tested and charged-for system. There is already early evidence of this happening as local authorities contract with health trusts for their services.

One of the direct consequences of the cost shunting of rehabilitation and care services is that the individual is shifted from a service which is free at the point of delivery to a service which is means-tested. Local authorities have discretionary powers to raise charges from clients who use their services (AMA and Local Government Information Unit, 1994). There are currently three charging options: no charge, a flat-rate charge on services irrespective of ability to pay, and a means test. There is considerable variation across authorities in the way charges are applied and for which services (AMA, 1994). As a result of rate capping and budget shortfalls the trend across all local authorities is towards an increase in charges for all services to a level above inflation, and the introduction of charges where none existed.

Total national spending on long-term care services for the elderly and physically disabled, both in NHS and care home settings (non-NHS), was estimated at £10.2 billion or 1.65 per cent of GDP in 1992. £9.1 billion was estimated to have been spent on the elderly, of which 30 per cent was generated through client contributions/charges. When the proportion of free NHS provision (27 per cent) for long-term care is excluded, the proportion from personal contributions rises to 41 per cent. It can be surmised that the transfer of responsibility away from NHS provision will increase the ratio of local taxation and patient charges to central funding, thereby further transferring costs to individuals and their communities (Laing, 1993).

The transfer of community care responsibility to local authorities will shift the risks and costs of care to a smaller tax base; the results of this transfer will almost inevitably be regressive. Areas with the greatest need will have to find the biggest sums of money from their resident communities and from client charges, and if they cannot raise these funds, poorer quality services will become the norm. This is a return to a pre-1948 system, when local authorities were responsible for raising local taxes to pay for health care. As then, current financing and charging policies create and perpetuate inequities, so that where you live determines what you pay and also what is provided.

HOW SHOULD WE RATION IN THE NHS?

Governments of all political complexions appear to want to reduce public expenditure and taxation. This has fast become part of the ideology of market driven systems where the individual chooses what they pay for and collective societal responsibilities disappear.

The move to a market-based system means that many of the advantages of the NHS have been lost. These included: low administration costs, high public accountability, a population focus for planning and evaluating the outcomes of care, stable geographic catchment populations, and services responsive to local communities. The possibilities for integrating care across health and social care have also been diminished by the fragmentation of purchasers. But there have also been other costs: the loss of a stable population related to a geographic area means the loss of data for assessing needs and evaluating service delivery and outcomes. And the US experience shows that markets and social goods are not compatible. It is no coincidence that Europe, Canada and Australia rejected the market in favour of universal coverage. For 50 years the NHS provided high quality services and universal access, and maintained the principle of services free at the point of delivery. In five years we have jettisoned these principles in favour of market led rationing where ability to pay and not need determines access to care.

Fine tuning and tinkering will not alter the inherent weaknesses of a market driven system; radical change is required. Health and social care funding mechanisms should be integrated and subject to common formulae. New structures are required to restore local accountability and the ability of the public to influence and improve local services. The growth in wasteful accounting and bureaucracy needs to be replaced with information-based planning and service evaluation. Above all, stable populations are required within geographically determined areas if the planning focus is to be restored. Only through planning and a population focus can equity be monitored and safeguarded. Only then can the fragmentation, duplication and chaos which results from the market be overcome. And only then can the public determine whether rationing is truly carried out on the basis of equal access for equal need.

I am grateful to Jennifer Dixon for her helpful comments and advice, without which this contribution would not have been possible.

References

Association of Community Health Councils for England and Wales, 'Fundholding and access to hospital care', 1994.

Association of Metropolitan Authorities, *A Survey of Social Services Charging Policies 1992-1994*, AMA, 1994.

Association of Metropolitan Authorities and Local Government Information Unit, 'Commentary on Social Services Inspectorate: advice note on discretionary charges for adult social services', AMA, 1994.

Beecham L., 'Fundholder's patients are treated quicker says BMA', *BMJ*, 308, 1994, p11.

Carpenter M., 'Normality is hard work', *Trade Unions and the Politics of Community Care*, UNISON, 1994.

Clarke A., McKee M., 'The consultant episode: an unhelpful measure', *BMJ*, 305, 1992, pp1307-8.

Critical Public Health, 'Careless talk costs lives', *Critical Public Health*, 4(1), 1993.

Department of Health, *Caring for People: community care in the next decade and beyond*, Policy Guidance, HMSO, London 1990.

Dixon J. M., Dinwoodie, Hodson D., *et al*, Distribution of NHS funds between fundholding and non-fundholding practices, *BMJ*, 309, 1994, pp30-35.

Dudley N. J., Burns E., 'The influence of age on policies for admission and thrombolysis in coronary care units in the United Kingdom', *Age and Ageing*, 21, 1992, pp95-98.

ISIS-2 (Second international study of infarct survival) Collaborative Group, 'Randomised trial of intravenous streptokinase, oral aspirin, both or neither among 17,187 cases of suspected acute myocardial infarction', *Lancet*, ii, 1988, pp349-60.

Klein R., 'Dimensions of rationing: who should do what?' *Rationing in Action*, chapter 9, pp96-104.

Klein R., 'On the Oregon trail: rationing health care', *BMJ*, 302, 1991, pp1-2.

Klein R., *The Politics of the NHS*, Longman, London 1983.

Laing W., *Financing Long-term Care: the crucial debate*, Age Concern, London 1993.

NAHAT, 'Sharing out resources. Purchasing and priority setting in the NHS', National Association of Health Authorities and Trusts, 1993.

NHS Management Executive, 'Local Voices, the views of local people in purchasing for health', NHMSE, 1992.

OPCS, Dental caries among children in the United Kingdom', OPCS, 1993.

Pfeffer N., Pollock A. M., 'Public Opinion and the NHS', *BMJ*, 307, 1993, pp750-751.

Pollock A. M., 'Public opinion and the NHS', *Critical Public Health*, 4(1), 1993.

Pollock A. M., Majeed A., 'Consultant episodes', *BMJ*, 306, 1993, pp14-2.

Pollock A. M., Pfeffer N., 'Doors of perception', *HSJ*, July 1993.

Pollock A. M., 'Local Voices: the bankruptcy of the democratic process', *BMJ*, 305, 1992, pp535-6.

Pollock A. M., 'The politics of destruction: rationing in the UK health care market', *Health Care Analysis*, 1995.

Pollock A. M., 'Where should health services go: local authorities versus the NHS?' *BMJ*, 310, 1995, pp1504-84.

President's letter to fellows and members of the Royal Society of Obstetricians and Gynaecologists, London 1994.

Raftery J., 'Capitation funding: population, age, and mortality adjustments for regional and district health authorities in England', *BMJ*, 307, 1993, pp1121-4.

Royal College of Surgeons of England, 'College Survey of Surgical Activity in the National Health Service', Royal College of Surgeons of England, London, January 1994.

Sheldon T., Smith P., Borowitz M., *et al*, 'Attempt at deriving a formula for setting general practitioner fundholding budgets', *BMJ*, 309, 1994, pp1059-65.

Smith P., Sheldon T., Carr-Hill R., *et al*, 'Allocating resources to health authorities: results and policy implications of small area analysis of use of in-patient services', *BMJ*, 309, 1994, pp1050-54.

Social Services Committee, 'First report, Resourcing the National

Health Service: short term issues', HMSO, London 1988.

Webster C., (ed), *Aneurin Bevin on the NHS*, Wellcome Unit for the History of Medicine, Oxford 1991.

COMMUNITY CARE:
PAST, PRESENT AND FUTURE

Alan Walker

Despite having recently undergone the most radical shake-up in nearly 50 years, community care provision is still failing to realise its considerable promise. Report after report - from Age Concern to the BMA, from the House of Commons Health Committee to the Association of Directors of Social Services - and television programme after television programme have come to the same conclusion as the Social Justice Commission: 'the condition of community care is a nightmare'. It was not coincidental that the title of the devastating BBC Panorama programme in November 1995, which exposed the shameful treatment of some frail older people discharged from hospital without adequate community support, used the same language as the Social Justice Commission: 'The Greatest Nightmare'. In fact this is a quotation from the Prime Minister's speech to the 1995 Conservative Party Conference, in which he promised that NHS support for older people would not be reduced because his elderly parents had relied on it so heavily.

Some of the reasons why community care is in such a nightmarish and discredited state are complex and longstanding and none of them were tackled by either the NHS and Community Care Act (1990) or the Griffiths Report that preceded it; in fact, in some respects, they made matters worse. Thus the first task of this chapter is to trace the failure of community care policy to match the considerable political rhetoric promoting it. The second is to examine the breaking of the post-war consensus on community care in the 1980s, and the impact of the introduction of a market philosophy to social care, followed by an assessment of the current condition of community care provision. Third, I identify the five key deficiencies - the 'floodgates' mentality; the limited concept of community care implicit in post-war policy; the dominance of professional or top-down models of care; the existence of age discrimination; and the recent subordination of care effectiveness to cost efficiency. Finally a new vision of community care is called for - one that sweeps away the flawed assumptions of the past and offers older people and their carers new opportunities for interdependent living in the community.

THE CONSENSUS YEARS 1944-1979

It is almost 50 years since the formation of the British welfare state and, although the 'fifth social service' - the personal social services - has always occupied a junior position compared with its four sisters, it is possible to identify the emergence of a clear commitment to community care very early in the life of the welfare state. Indeed, a preference for community care on the part of policymakers may be traced back to the turn of the century when the Local Government Board recommended 'more homely' accommodation than the workhouse (PSSC/ CHSC, 1978, p.6). The principle was first enunciated in the post-war period by the Curtis Committee (1946) with regard to children, and the principle was enacted by the 1948 Children's Act. Similar proposals soon followed with regard to older people, but the key difference when compared with policy towards children was the absence of legislative commitment (Parker, 1964). Domiciliary services for older people were not regarded as a priority and were left largely to the voluntary sector (Means and Smith, 1994, p25). Thus the build-up of local authority services was haphazard and provision patchy.

However, while the reality consisted of a paucity of services, in terms of both levels and quality, politicians had begun to realise the power of the concept of community care and it appeared with increasing regularity throughout the 1950s on political platforms and in official reports. The frequent use of the term emphasised both the gulf between rhetoric and reality in post-war community care policy and the inherent danger in letting policymakers loose with a concept that is heavily overloaded with ambiguity and brimming with moral and social connotations. As Titmuss pointed out so clearly, in a lecture given 34 years ago, over-frequent use of such terms may actually hinder progress by giving the impression that the goal has been achieved:

> It has been one of the more interesting characteristics of the English in recent years to employ idealistic terms to describe certain branches of public policy ... It is necessary to remember ... that this practice can have unfortunate consequences ... In the public mind the aspirations of reformers are transmitted, by the touch of a phrase, into hard-won reality. What some hope will one day exist is suddenly thought by many to exist already. (Titmuss, 1968, p.105)

Nonetheless, the term proved irresistible to politicians and it was employed frequently, but there was never a consistent programme of resource allocation to accompany the rhetoric (Walker, 1982). For example the major report *Health and Welfare* presented figures showing that local authorities were not making any new preparations for an expansion of community care. Their plans revealed that residential staff were due to increase at nearly twice the rate of home helps between 1962 and 1972 (Ministry of Health, 1963, p46).

In practice, therefore, even the limited goal of care *in* the community by domiciliary services was, by the early 1960s, already compromised. Subsequent official statements and policies did not provide any sustained attempt to define and measure the need for community care, nor did they set policy goals and then relate those goals to the scale of need and the allocation of resources. In other words, there was a complete absence of planning for the development of community care services. Yet still the promise of community care was frequently reiterated. In 1976, for example, an explicit commitment was made by the then DHSS (1976, p8) to services 'which aim to help people to live an independent life in their own homes as long as possible'.

Thus, to take stock, the immediate post-war period saw the establishment of the basic principles of community care - the maintenance of those in need within familiar surroundings and the provision of support in the home from a range of services in order to prevent unnecessary admission to a residential home or hospital - and a considerable amount of rhetorical backing for these principles on the part of politicians of both main parties. In fact it is difficult to discern any significant difference between the parties on this issue. However, despite political consensus, the policy itself remained precarious throughout this period. It was never defined in any of the key statutes - from the National Assistance Act (1948) to the Chronically Sick and Disabled Persons Act (1970) - and, equally importantly, sufficient resources were never allocated, or re-allocated from institutional care, to enable the promises to be fulfilled. In fact residential care continued to take the lion's share of local authority PSS budgets over the whole of the period and, partly as a consequence, there was a considerable shortfall in the supply of community care services.

It may be considered surprising that the post-war party political consensus on community care policy survived for so long but this may be explained by its largely symbolic nature and the very low priority it was accorded compared with other sectors of the welfare state. To paraphrase Edelman (1977) the words succeeded magnificently but the policy itself was a failure. As a result excessive expectations were placed on families, and female kin in particular, and community care interests remained subordinated to institutional interests in both the health and social services. Nonetheless there was a consensus among policymakers on both the secondary role of the formal sector to the informal sector and on the premise that when services were provided in the community the most appropriate location for the planning, organisation and delivery of these services was SSDs. This does not mean that local authorities were exclusive providers of social care; there has always been a mixed system of welfare in this field. But the mixture was very unbalanced, with local SSDs being the dominant providers and the voluntary and private sectors occupying limited roles either independently or, more usually, under contract from SSDs.

FROM CONSENSUS TO CONFLICT 1979-1995

So, after more than 30 years of community care policy, by the late 1970s the failure to extend social services provision in response to rising need (created largely by demographic change) had resulted in a growing 'care gap' between the need for care and the provision of domiciliary services (Walker, 1985). This meant that the amount of care provided by the informal sector of family, friends and neighbours was increasing and, moreover, institutional budgets continued to dominate both health and social services (Gray, Whelan and Normand, 1988). Then on to the stage came urgent economic pressures, stemming initially from the fiscal crisis of the mid 1970s but given a particular anti-welfare state slant following the election of the Thatcher government. These processes produced severe budgetary and resource constraints and the cost-effectiveness imperative which, combined with a major expansion of need for care particularly among very elderly people, created the political will to overcome both the policy inertia and power struggle between sectional interests that had underpinned the precarious consensus on community care. But the policy itself departed significantly from the previous consensus. Thus the emphasis was purposely shifted away from care *in* the community supported by local authority personnel, towards a confusing mixture of care *by* the community itself and private care, regardless of whether in domiciliary or institutional settings.

Signs that the post-war consensus on community care policy was about to be destroyed became apparent soon after the election of the first Thatcher government. In contrast to its predecessors it was characterised by an overt neo-liberal (or new right) ideology and this remained the driving force behind the policy throughout the 1980s. The government's first public expenditure White Paper (Treasury, 1979) combined with a speech by the Secretary of State for Social Services (Jenkin, 1979) marked a radical break with the past - the ending of protected status for personal social services (PSS) spending, the abandonment of the co-ordination and monitoring of local service provision, and the increasing reliance on non-statutory forms of welfare (Webb and Wistow, 1982; Walker, 1986) - a trend which was confirmed subsequently by a series of official reports and statements culminating in the NHS and Community Care Act, 1990.

Three intertwined developments characterised policy in this field in the 1980s. The first was the promotion of the private sector (Walker, 1989). This was achieved by reducing the resources available to local authorities and using rate-capping to enforce the policy; and, while the public sector received the stick, the private sector was offered a carrot. The rest, as they say, is history: the 1980s witnessed the largest upsurge in private sector residential and nursing home places of this century. The social security budget fuelling this increase became the fastest growing item of public expenditure: from £10 million in 1979, to £1.2 billion in 1991, to well over £2 billion in 1995.

Second, the government embarked upon a radical programme of long-stay mental hospital closure. This was a desirable policy in principle - and one that had been proclaimed by successive secretaries of state for health - but until 1986, not one hospital had been closed. Unfortunately, the political will to achieve hospital closures came chiefly from the desire to reduce public expenditure, and plenty of evidence is available to show that this has resulted in people being relocated without adequate preparation, particularly the mentally ill (House of Commons Social Services Committee, 1985).

Third, the government attempted to residualise the social services - to turn local authority SSDs from being the main providers of formal care into something far more limited: the providers of those residual services which no-one else could or would take on. The first Thatcherite Secretary of State, Patrick Jenkin, outlined a residual role for the social services in 1980: 'a long-stop for the very special needs going beyond the range of voluntary services' (Jenkin, 1980). Ominously, in 1981, the White Paper on Older People asserted that 'care in the community must increasingly mean care *by* the community' (DHSS, 1981, p.6). Then, in 1984, Norman Fowler mapped out a decidedly minimalist position for the PSS when he said that their main role was 'to back-up and develop the assistance which is given by private and voluntary support'.

Meanwhile the social security budget was spiralling out of control and an influential report by the Audit Commission pronounced that 'community care policies are in some disarray'. The Commission highlighted the 'perverse incentive' for older people requiring care to enter residential homes, despite the proclaimed policy of community care. Sir Roy Griffiths was appointed, in March 1987, to clean up the mess. His report was published in March 1988, the White Paper *Caring for People* followed in November 1989 and, within days, the NHS and Community Care Bill was published. The awarding of lead agency status to SSDs - by first Griffiths, then the white paper and finally the 1990 Act - may seem to be at odds with the residualisation strategy I have just outlined. However, Griffiths made a clear distinction between responsibility for ensuring that care is provided and its actual provision: 'the role of the public sector is essentially to ensure that care is provided. How it is provided is an important but secondary consideration'. Thus the role of local authorities was recast as one of management and regulation rather than direct provision. The stipulation that 85 per cent of the special transitional grant for community care must be spent in the non-statutory sectors was designed to enforce the residualisation of public sector provision.

Ministerial attention in the latter part of the 1980s and early 1990s was focused almost exclusively on the organisation of community care and, specifically, the creation of an internal market based on the purchaser/provider split. Nonetheless, the promise of community care and, following the 1990 Act, an increased influence over care decisions, were still held out to service users and their family carers. In 1981 the DHSS argued that 'most people who need long-term care can and should be looked after in the community. This is what most of them want for themselves and what those responsible for their care believe to be best'. By the end of the decade the government was not only reiterating its firm commitment to community care but was also promising both practical support for informal carers and that service users, or consumers in the language of the market, would be given 'a greater individual say in how they live their lives and the services they need to help them to do so' (D.H., 1989, p4).

What has been the impact of this policy? This question can be answered with reference to the largest group of service users: older people. As in the period of consensus, while there is ample political rhetoric to quote, the achievements up to and following the implementation in 1993 of the NHS and Community Care Act have been minimal. Indeed the perverse incentive resulted in the *over*-supply of residential care places and, in contrast, a tighter and tighter rationing of home care. Over the decade 1979-1989 the numbers of beds in the private residential sector trebled, to 31.1 places per 1000 people over 65. Yet it is estimated that only 11 places per 1000 people over the age of 65 are required to support severely disabled older people. Thus a significant proportion of older people in private residential homes, perhaps as much as one-half, do not need to occupy residential places on the basis of disability. The implications of this development for the social status and citizenship of older people are profound. For example, substantial numbers of them have entered and are still entering residential homes because there is no reliable community-based alternative and no funding for them to buy their own. As a result, this group prematurely encounters the dependency-creating aspects of residential regimes (Walker, 1982). Moreover the rapid expansion of the private sector has been skewed towards the younger age groups of older people in which need is less than among the very elderly. For instance, between 1979 and 1989 there was a 38 per cent growth in the numbers aged 85 and over and this was accompanied by a 12 per cent rise in the number of private residential beds; yet while the population aged 65-74 declined by 9 per cent there was a 15 per cent growth in private provision for this group. In other words, the uncontrolled expansion of the private sector militated against the distribution of services according to need.

Some policy analysts (see for example Day and Klein, 1987) have taken the view that the growth of the private sector of residential care is beneficial because it increases choice in an expanding 'mixed economy of welfare'. Indeed, the appeal to increased choice has proved an important source of popular legitimation for the fast expansion of the private sector. However, while it is true that there has been a rapid multiplication of private homes, as a result of the government's residualisation strategy local authority residential places have been cut for all groups of older people, especially those aged 85 and over, and the building of sheltered housing for older people has fallen sharply. Yet genuine choice requires a range of alternative forms of care: public sector homes, day care, the opportunity to remain in an ordinary dwelling with community support. But ironically, this sort of choice has been severely restricted by the 'perverse incentive' (Audit Commission, 1986) for older people to enter residential care created by social security payments and perpetuated to some extent by the 85 per cent rule. Furthermore, when it comes to entering a residential home the concept of 'choice' is rarely appropriate. The need for residential care usually arises because of a crisis of care in the informal sector, leaving little time to 'shop around' for alternatives. Thus, as Bradshaw (1988) has confirmed, the promise of choice held out by the supporters of the private sector is often illusory.

There is a growing body of evidence that the creation of a large private residential care sector has not resulted in greater choice as the proponents of this policy had claimed. For example, a study of the private sector by the Centre for Policy on Ageing found that only a quarter of residents exercised any choice about the home they were admitted to, while nearly a quarter said that their admission resulted from unsolicited arrangements by a third party (Bradshaw, 1988, p18). Choice between private homes is severely restricted by factors such as geographical location, waiting lists and ability to pay. There is also research evidence showing that residents are not able to exercise much choice once they are inside this major sector of welfare. For example, homes may be bought and sold without reference to the residents and the character of the home as well as an individual's living arrangements may be altered without consultation.

THE CURRENT STATE OF COMMUNITY CARE

This brings me to the current state of community care. On top of the care gap that existed at the end of the 1970s, a tighter and tighter rationing of community care budgets has been imposed with the result that in many places, support is available only for those in greatest need. Frail older people who, in previous decades, would have expected to receive some assistance are now being denied any. Instead family, friends and neighbours are being expected to provide care that should be the responsibility of the statutory authorities. The 85 per cent rule covering the special transitional grant has meant that, in the absence of a significant private domiciliary sector, there is still a perverse incentive for older people to enter residential homes, and the restrictions on fee levels, coupled with the enforcement of the more stringent means test, has forced relatives and older people themselves to contribute towards the cost of long-term care. There are numerous instances of people selling their homes to finance residential care. This policy development was never discussed openly, it has never figured in an election campaign, yet it has enormous implications for intergenerational relationships within the family.

Despite the huge amount of rhetoric about the new role of the social services consumer and listening to the views of carers - and I do not want to underestimate the usefulness of much of the national profile that has been given to the needs of carers nor the considerable efforts made by some local authorities to involve service users - the fact is that the vast majority of people needing care, particularly those being discharged from hospital, do not have any choice in the matter. Local authority care managers have been put in an impossible position of being expected to take on board the views of users while having to keep within budgets that are declining relative to the growth in need created by population ageing. What was trumpeted as a new needs-led service has quickly reverted to one which attempts to meet needs within tightly controlled and inadequate budgets. Not surprisingly, resources are being focused only on those with the most pressing needs and, as a consequence, the possibility of preventive and rehabilitative work is being reduced.

Commenting in 1989 on the White Paper *Caring for People*, I argued that its proposed strategy, including the introduction of means tests, could only be understood by reference to the health White Paper *Working for Patients* which sought to reduce the role of the NHS in providing free care, particularly for older people. The operation of the internal market in the NHS is forcing the discharge of patients who are both unfit and lacking adequate community support. All too predictably there is now competition in some areas between health and social services to avoid the most costly frail older people and, as a consequence, community care has been reduced to a grotesque parody in which frail and vulnerable people are being shunted in and out of hospital as the NHS seeks to disown them. In this situation the thousands of dedicated and caring staff in the health and social services are finding that their desire to provide high quality care is being swamped by the huge needs that confront them and the inadequacy of the resources at their disposal. The resulting impact on their morale and physical and mental health reinforces the downward spiral that community care is currently in. The only surprise is that such staff are able to maintain the quality of the care they provide.

The assessment system that lies at the heart of the post-April 1993 policy is discredited already. Unlike its role model, medical assessment, there is no guarantee of a service response. Therefore local authority care managers are placed in an invidious position: they cannot assess need with regard to specific services if they are unable, in fact, to meet the need, otherwise they risk legal action by the person they have assessed. In these circumstances it is virtually impossible for managers to be honest with service users and their carers.

It is not surprising that the current state of community care has been described as a nightmare, a term that I do not regard as melodramatic in this context. This is certainly the correct term to describe the experiences of the many frail and vulnerable people that are in limbo between the NHS and social services; it is also correct to describe in this way the situation of family carers, often old and frail themselves, being driven to the end of their endurance by the need to provide 24-hour care to a spouse or parent, especially if that person is suffering from depression, confusion or dementia. These personal nightmares, often borne in isolation, provide an indictment of the whole system of social care and one that must be addressed as a matter of urgency.

DEFICIENCIES IN BRITISH COMMUNITY CARE POLICY

How is it that the idealistic dream of community care, born in the immediate post-war period, which has been the subject of countless promises by successive governments over the last half-century has been reduced to a position in which, for the vast majority of people in need there is effectively *no* community care? Indeed, over the last 50 years, the proportion of people aged 65 and over resident in homes or long-stay hospitals has actually increased. Some of the reasons for this failure to realise the dream of community care are longstanding while others were introduced during the last 15 years. There are five main ones to consider.

In the first place, there is the obsessive 'floodgates' mentality which holds that if a high quality community care service is provided families will leave everything to the state and, as a consequence, spending will go through the roof. This fear has featured significantly in all post-war community care policies, yet there is no scientific evidence to sustain it. Indeed what evidence there is demonstrates that families remain the front-line providers of care (particularly female kin) regardless of what support is available externally. The research that Hazel Qureshi and I conducted in Sheffield revealed a complex process of decision-making within families concerning the care of older relatives, with social services being regarded as the last, not the first, resort (Qureshi and Walker, 1989). Others have reached similar conclusions about the continuation of the close bonds between older people and their families and the willingness of relatives, where they are available, to provide care. The 'floodgates' mentality is based on ignorance of the sociology of family relationships and, particularly, the operation of reciprocity between the generations and is, frankly, insulting to millions of caring relatives.

What is happening, however, and what recent policies have failed to recognise is that the nature of both the caring relationship and the family itself are changing rapidly. As a result of increased longevity families are having to care over longer and longer periods but the ability (not the willingness) of kin to provide such care is being constrained by socio-demographic changes such as the reduction in family size, the ageing of spouse carers, the increase in female labour-force participation, and the rise in the divorce rate. Therefore families require more support, not less, if they are to sustain their caring relationships.

Unfortunately fears about opening the floodgates have confined community care to a very limited back-stop or casualty service. This has had several negative consequences. It has weighed particularly heavily on women, who are more likely than men to provide personal and domestic care, and has reinforced gender-based inequalities in the distribution of informal care. It has prevented the practice of community care from realising its full potential with regard to prevention and rehabilitation. These functions have hardly got started in the last 50 years, yet they can be vital in maintaining an individual in the community. As the Alzheimer's Disease Society told the House of Commons Health Committee in 1994:

> an hour of care a week for a carer for someone with Alzheimer's disease who is in the early stages may be enough to keep that person out of hospital for a very long time, but if they have no care at all critically because they are not considered to be severely in need, then you are always in a state of crisis management...

The British approach to community care has placed too much responsibility on family carers and, paradoxically therefore, it has contributed to the likelihood that caring relationships will break down.

European comparisons provide some indication of the potential for a more effective partnership between the family and the state in the care of vulnerable people. Denmark has the most developed home care provision in the EU with three times as many home carers as in the UK. For example, in

Denmark more than two-thirds of older people receiving care are getting help from the social services compared with only a quarter in the UK. In contrast, just over two-fifths of Danish older people are being helped by their families compared with three-fifths in the UK (Walker, Guillemard and Alber, 1993; Walker, 1993). It cannot be concluded from this data that Denmark's superior community care provision has resulted in a reduction in family care because community care is viewed in part as a mechanism to support the economic independence of women. Comparisons of family contact show similar patterns between the two countries, suggesting that community care does not result in the desertion of older people by their families (Walker, 1993).

Second, as indicated already the concept of community care that has been pursued in the last 50 years is a very limited one indeed, amounting, at best, to a few hours home help support *in* the community. Thus the potential for community care to operate in partnership with families to support their caring activities has not been allowed to develop. Also the exclusion of key services such as health and housing from the narrow social services definition of community care has resulted in endless attempts to improve co-ordination, all of which have failed. The pursuit of community care is constantly bedevilled by the absence of integrated planning and, as a result, there are frequent policy conflicts with other departments. The Department of the Environment's withdrawal of urban programme funding, which has undermined the ability of some voluntary organisations to take part in local community care initiatives, is just one example among many (Health Committee, 1993).

The need for active community support and community development has never been part of the British approach to community care. Similarly, the connection between economic policy and community care - the extent to which care *by* the community depends on care *for* the community - has not been recognised because community care for older people has been ghettoised within the lowly fifth social service. We have heard a great deal recently from the leaders of both main political parties about the importance of community, but there is no analysis of what a community consists of and certainly no suggestions as to the role of the community in the care of frail people. What is clear from experience, however, is that if politicians base their care policies on an over-idealised notion of the community - 'care *in* the community must increasingly mean care *by* the community' - they will succeed only in over-burdening the family.

Third, the British approach to community care has always been dominated by the perspective of service providers rather than that of users. The medical model of professional dominance was built into the structure of service planning and provision and, as a consequence, the views of service users and their carers were squeezed out. In fact, too much power has been allocated to professionals within the health and social services and their training has encouraged practice based on the idea of autonomous expertise. Politicians were guilty of, in effect, handing over to social care professionals the responsibility for creating welfare. The exclusion of service users and potential users and carers from active participation in the vital decisions concerning the nature of their care has had an important effect on the quality of services, which do not always reflect the needs of users. In political terms too, a coalition between service providers and service users has been prevented. This issue concerns the basic human rights of vulnerable people to be consulted properly about their care needs.

In the NHS and Community Care Act (1990) and subsequent policy guidance, the government responded to the mounting criticism from users and carers groups that services are unresponsive to their needs by creating the concept of the social services consumer. Unfortunately the rhetoric concerning user involvement and empowerment that accompanied the introduction of this policy often lost touch with the far more limited reality of the notion of consumerism in practice. In the absence of clear guidelines for the achievement of user involvement and in the presence of severe resource constraints it was always likely that professional opinions would continue to dominate care decisions, and so it has proved. Rather than determining their own packages of care, service users are apparently still seen officially as passive receivers of care, or 'cases' to be 'managed'. In fact, when viewed from the perspective of service users, the conception of user involvement underlying current policies is a very restricted one based on a simplistic market analogy (Walker, 1991a, 1992). The Griffiths Report, White Paper and the NHS and Community Care Act all derive from the limited form of supermarket-style consumerism which assumes that, if there is a choice between 'products', service users will automatically have the power of exit from a particular product or market. Of course, even if this is true in markets for consumer goods, in the field of social care many people are mentally disabled, frail and vulnerable, they are not in a position to 'shop around' and have no realistic prospect of exit.

Fourth, partly as a consequence of provider domination, community care policy and practice have exhibited discriminatory attitudes, particularly towards older people. For example, there is the ready acceptance of institutional care as appropriate for older people when it was rejected as long ago as 1946 with regard to children. The unified social service departments, established following the Seebohm Report (1968), were soon monopolised by child care issues, a bias that was reinforced by each of the long series of inquiries into the death of children and the resulting statutory guidance or legislation. Research has shown that SSDs operated with client group hierarchies, with older people at the bottom (Bowl, 1986). Social work with older people has been regarded as routine and low priority.

The continuation of these ageist attitudes has been exposed by research examining the quality of life of older people with learning difficulties. For example, research in the north-west has shown that the service principles applied to people with learning difficulties, such as normalisation and the right to an ordinary life, are overturned with regard to older people with learning difficulties in favour of the ageist assumption of a service continuum from day care, to domiciliary care, to residential care. Thus the quality of life of a person with learning difficulties and the support they may expect from the social services depends critically on their age (Walker, Walker and Ryan, 1994). Why it is that liberating concepts such as normalisation and community integration are only applied to younger adults?

These fundamental flaws in the British approach to community care were either built into the system or have evolved as part of it over the past 50 years. The fifth and final defect has been added only recently. I am referring to the introduction of market or quasi-market principles into the organisation and delivery of community care. The application of a market philosophy to care is mistaken and is bound to fail because, unlike the market for consumer goods, there are not multiple purchasers and providers on the one hand, nor active consumers on the other. In most areas the local authority and health authority are the only public purchasers and, in an attempt to overcome this deficiency, the government rigged the market. The purposive duplication required to create a wide range of alternative providers would be an act of madness in a field where high quality skilled caring staff are at a premium. Moreover, the government's obsession with provider diversity missed the key point, which concerns the *quality* of the care provided. As Jill Pitkeathley, director of the Carers Association, said to the 1994 House of Commons Health Committee inquiry into community care: 'your normal community care user as carer does not know or care who provides the services; it is the quality of the service that is important to them'.

It is the imposition of market principles, coupled with the hurried removal of long-term care functions from the NHS and the forceful application of the crudest form of least-cost efficiency, that has brought the community care system to its current state of crisis. Moreover, fears have been expressed, for example to the House of Commons Health Committee (1993), that once that it had established the new system and was able to tightly control budgets centrally - while leaving operational responsibility with local authorities - the government washed its hands of community care.

CREATING A NEW VISION FOR COMMUNITY CARE

Having indicated how community care got into its current predicament, we must consider how to release it so that it can enjoy a brighter future. Any such consideration of future directions must, of necessity, recognise that the need for long-term care is growing and adequate preparations are required because, as noted earlier, the care potential of the family is shrinking. Thus Germany has just introduced a new system of public insurance for long-term care, paid for in the same way as pensions.

The Social Justice Commission (1994) examined the issue of the future of long-term care and rejected the 'deregulators' market solution because it would cover only a minority of the population. The private care insurance market has been developed most fully in the US, but even in that country only 3 per cent of older people currently have long-term care insurance (Wiener, 1990, p33). All of the major studies conducted in the US have concluded that only a minority of older people can afford such insurance and the same is likely to be true in Britain. According to a recent review of long-term care in the US: 'Expansions of public programs or very deep subsidies for the purchase of private insurance are needed to protect the elderly against the catastrophic costs of long-term care' (Wiener, 1990, p34).

The Commission's favoured 'investors' approach is mixture of private and public insurance. However, this overlooks the deficiencies of current insurance systems - public and private - especially the exclusion of large numbers of low-paid women; the practical difficulties of transplanting a Bismarckian policy to a Beveridge-based welfare state; and the preference of the British public for a system of social care provided in kind and funded by taxation. We asked the general public in each EU country about the best way of providing for long-term care and the British public were decidedly lukewarm with regard to both private and public insurance - only 4 per cent favoured the former and 18 per cent the latter, while 57 per cent thought that public provision financed through taxation was the best way (Walker, 1993).

Unfortunately the Social Justice Commission also accepted uncritically some questionable assumptions about the rising cost of long-term care. Most damning of all, however, is that the Commission focused solely on the issue of finance and, therefore, it failed to tackle the fundamental matter of social justice concerning *access* to community care. Thus the Commission's approach would perpetuate most of the underlying deficiencies of Britain's community care legacy.

It is time for a new vision of community care for older people and other groups. This would comprise, first of all, a recognition of the vital role that social care may play in the *prevention* of family breakdown and in improving the quality of life of older people and their family carers. This means a substantial expansion in home care facilities - Denmark provides three times as many home carers per 1000 people aged 65 and over as does the UK. The economic contribution of this effort must be emphasised, in terms of job creation and support for full-time workers, as well as the financial cost. There is plenty of research evidence to show that high cost institutional care can be avoided by well targetted community care, but the latter will not work if it is done on the cheap.

Second, it is essential to erase the discriminatory aspects of community care practice and to offer older people in particular the same opportunities as other groups for supported independent living.

Third, community care services must be distributed according to clear principles, such as rights of access and the right of the service users to take part in decisions concerning their care. This means that service providers and managers have to be trained to empower service users. However, it will not be possible to achieve such empowerment within current budgets. Already some two-fifths of social services departments are admitting that they are having to ration severely community care funds.

Fourth, the most appropriate mechanism for financing long-term care in this country remains general taxation. This enables both that risk may be spread throughout society and that solidarity between the generations can be expressed. It is important, too, for policymakers to reconsider the organisational division between primary health and social care because it makes very little sense with regard to long-term care. The idea of local authorities holding dual responsibility for commissioning both health and social care is an attractive option but would entail a massive upheaval in the NHS. An alternative, less disruptive path would be the establishment of joint commissioning authorities between health and social services and, at the time of writing, it looks as if the Labour Party will move in this direction.

CONCLUSION

At its most basic community care is an appealing, even noble, concept (and this is, in part, the cause of its downfall). It is right that people needing care should be assisted to remain in their own homes or in a familiar neighbourhood for as long as possible. This is what countless surveys show that both service users and their relatives desire. Society as a whole has a duty to ensure that people remain integrated socially, rather than segregated.

Unfortunately, the idealism associated with community care in its infancy has been destroyed by the shameless use of the concept in policy and practice over the last 50 years. Its meaning has been redefined frequently to suit the ideological predilections of the day and, for too long, insufficient resources have been provided to achieve it. Thus, in practice, this cosy phrase has acted as a cover for society's neglect of the care needs of vulnerable people, for the exploitation of family care, and for age discriminatory attitudes.

However, it does not have to be that way, as is demonstrated by the success of some innovations in the care of older people and of people with learning difficulties, and by the high quality of the care provided in some other countries.

In order to reclaim the concept of community care as a noble principle on which to base long-term care it is important to remember that it was introduced in the first place to emphasise the idea that it should be abnormal for people to live in communal surroundings designed for the purposes of care, or rather tending. Instead it projected a vision of continuing care in a familiar environment. Community care is a potentially vital source of social integration, and has a key role to play in promoting the right of all citizens to self-determination. To realise this vision there must be an open partnership between the state and the family.

References

Audit Commission, *Making a Reality of Community Care*, PSI, London 1986.

Bowl R., 'Social Work with Old People' in C. Phillipson and A. Walker (eds), *Ageing and Social Policy*, Gower, Aldershot 1986, pp128-145.

Bradshaw J., 'Financing Private Care for the Elderly', Department of Social Policy and Social Work, University of York 1988.

Day P. and Klein R., 'The Business of Welfare', *New Society*, 19 June 1987, pp11-13.

DH, *Caring for People*, Cmnd 849, HMSO, London 1989.

DHSS, *Priorities for Health and Personal Social Services*, HMSO, London 1976.

DHSS, *Growing Older*, Cmnd 8173, HMSO, London 1981.

Edelman M., *Political Language*, Academic Press, New York 1977.

Gray, A.M., Whelan A., and Normand C., *Care in the Community: A Study of Services and Costs in Six Districts*, Centre for Health Economics, University of York, 1988.

Griffiths Sir R., *Community Care: Agenda for Action*, HMSO, London 1988.

House of Commons Health Committee, *Community Care: The Way Forward*, Vol 1, HMSO, London 1993.

House of Commons Social Services Committee, *Community Care*, HMSO, London 1985.

Jenkin P., *Speech to Social Services Conference*, Bournemouth, 21 November 1979.

Jenkin P., *Speech to the Conference of the Association of Directors of Social Services*, 19 September 1980.

Means R., and Smith R., *Community Care*, Macmillan, London 1994.

Ministry of Health, *Health and Welfare: the Development of Community Care*, Cmnd 1973, HMSO, London 1963.

Parker J., *Local Health and Welfare Services*, Allen & Unwin, London 1964.

PSSC/CHSC, *Collaboration in Community Care - A Discussion Document*, HMSO, London 1978.

Qureshi H., and Walker A., *The Caring Relationship*, Macmillan, London 1989.

Seebohm Committee, *Report of the Committee on Local Authority and Allied Personal Social Services*, Cmnd 3703, HMSO, London 1968.

Social Justice Commission, *Social Justice*, Vintage Books, London 1994.

Titmuss R.M., *Commitment to Welfare*, Allen & Unwin, London 1968.

Treasury, *The government's Expenditure Plans 1980/81*, Cmnd 7746, HMSO, London 1979.

Walker A. (ed), *Community Care*, Basil Blackwell, Oxford 1982.

Walker A., *The Care Gap*, Local Government Information Unit, London 1985.

Walker A., 'More Ebbs Than Flows', *Social Services Insight*, 29 March 1986, pp16-17.

Walker A., 'Community Care' in M. McCarthy (ed), *The New Politics of Welfare*, Macmillan, London 1989, pp205-25.

Walker A., 'Increasing User Involvement in the Social Services' in T. Arie (ed), *Recent Advances in Psychogeriatrics 2*, Churchill Livingstone, London 1991.

Walker A., 'Towards a European Agenda in Home Care for Older People: Convergencies and Controversies' in A. Evers and G. van der Zanden (eds), *Better Care for Dependent People Living at Home: Meeting the New Agenda in Services for the Elderly*, Netherlands Institute of Gerontology (forthcoming).

Walker A., *Age and Attitudes*, European Commission, Brussels 1993.

Walker A., Guillemard A-M. and Alber J., *Older People in Europe - Social and Economic Policies*, European Commission, Brussels 1993.

Walker A., Walker C., and Ryan A., 'Older People or People with

Learning Difficulties?', *Ageing and Society* (forthcoming).

Webb A. and Wistow G., 'The Personal Social Services: Incrementalism, Expediency or Systematic Social Planning?' in A. Walker (ed), *Public Expenditure and Social Policy*, Heinemann, London 1982, pp137-164.

Wiener J.M. and Harris K.M., 'Myths and Realities', *The Brookings Review*, Fall 1990, pp29-34.

FUTURE OPTIONS FOR THE NHS

Steve Iliffe and James Munro

THE LONG MARCH CONTINUES

Who envies the next Health Minister? The problems of the NHS are now so profound, and so wide-ranging, that the post of Secretary of State for Northern Ireland would appear a softer option. What could the new minister do, given the changes introduced over the last 17 years, and in particular since 1990?

There is almost certainly no going back, in the sense of simply restoring the old 'command and control' structure of the NHS. The service has suffered too much perturbation to tolerate further potentially destabilising re-organisation driven by ideology. Staff morale would not improve, in the short term anyway, by reshuffling the management structures, and too many of the advantages latent in the current situation would be lost. The emphasis must be on consolidation and stabilisation, with slow, incremental changes in most areas of policy, but an enthusiasm for making the most of some of the paradoxical opportunities that Thatcher and Major governments have unwittingly created.

EXPLOITING OPPORTUNITIES

The purchaser-provider split has taken direct control of strategic planning away from hospital chiefs and in principle allows resources to be redirected towards community-based services, or even further upstream, towards health promotion and preventive action. Powerful hospitals can still dominate the planning agenda and short-circuit the resource allocation process by opening their doors ever wider to the public to draw in more patients, but their renewed orientation to their communities is in itself a gain. The poverty of public health medicine, and its distance from the populations it seeks to serve, are also obstacles to the effective separation of strategic planning and service delivery, but both can be remedied in the medium term by the approaches outlined in Alison McCallum's chapter.

A continuation of the debate about rationing will strengthen the position of the strategic planning agencies, provided that they are willing to reduce the 'democratic deficit' by approaching and engaging with their local populations. This will not happen through the distribution of glossy brochures full of histograms, but through the development and maintainance of relationships with civil society - the schools, churches, trades unions and other 'voluntary organisations' that are the skeleton of local communities. Such activity is expensive in time, but without it the emotive power of the local hospital could overwhelm the planning impetus. The Health Minister will need to resource this approach, and take the risk that politicisation of debates around rationing could drum up trade for the private sector.

Management of clinical activities by non-clinicians is never popular with professionals, but it is integral to the wider accountability that must permeate the NHS if it is to balance demand for services against a given budget. The relationship between managers and clinicians will evolve gradually and no doubt unevenly, expressing the usefulness of 'conflict partnership'[1] or 'contestability' in promoting slow change at every level, from the individual health centre to negotiations between strategic planners and providers.

The relationship between planners and providers, and between clinicians and managers, cannot and should not be perfect, but it must be open. The need to draw social and health care together has been evident for decades, but it has now become possible with the purchaser-provider split, if the purchaser has the opportunity to purchase (and therefore plan) all care. The right favours total purchasing by independent contractor general practitioners, who will evolve into a hybrid of Health Maintainance Organisations and mini-health authorities through merger and economies of scale, but without a shred of public accountability beyond an overview by 'outposts' of the vestigial NHS Executive. As a compromise, the 'moderate' right would settle for interim total purchasing by the present commissioning agency quangos, whilst pumping resources into general practitioner multi-funds. A left-wing Health Minister, therefore, should favour the transfer of all purchasing to local government, and work to that end, as Alison Pollock proposes. Professional hostility to control by local government will not vanish, but tension is integral to 'conflict partnership' and local government will not employ clinicians, nor own hospitals or practices, so the old feud between doctors and the local state may not prevent such change. A greater risk is that Conservative local governments will attempt to impose divisive and inequitable requirements on local health services (like discrimination against drug users or AIDS patients with unwholesome backgrounds), or simply try to save money. Such maverick activity could be avoided by insisting on adherence to national guidelines and targets. By an irony of history the Conservatives have created a situation in which an old socialist objective - local government control of the NHS - could come about and be protected against local subversion through the mechanisms pioneered by the *Health of the Nation* and the *Patients' Charter*.

Fundholding is a way-station to a new kind of health service, with potent capacity to destabilise the health care market and an in-built bias towards inequity in provision. It will not last in its present configuration, but the emergence of multi-funds that could eclipse the remnants of commissioning agencies is a distinct possibility. The fundholding experiment, therefore, should be terminated, to restore stability, preserve equity and keep long-term planning as near as possible to the democratic power and as far as possible from commerce. The invaluable expertise developed by fundholders, however, is a commodity needed by the NHS, and should be recruited for the locality planning structures that are emerging. Fundholding ideology and unity will both dissolve if the leading figures get the jobs, roles and resources they seek, and their mouths are stuffed with power rather than with gold.

The Conservative agenda in prioritising health promotion

may have been part a cynical diversion of public and professional attention from their other plans for the NHS, and in part an attempt to foster a culture of self-reliance and victim-blaming, prior to wholesale privatisation of the health service; but it has created an interesting opportunity that Bevan would have relished. The danger in health promotion is that it will suffer 'provider capture' and become a task that professionals perform on the public - the immunisation approach, without effective vaccines for heart disease or much else - rather than become part of the function of civil society. Both the public and the professions contain interest groups that will naturally perceive health promotion in commodity terms, as something that a service can deliver. Some will go a step further, and trade in commodities in the market place. A strong ethic of social engineering exists in the medical profession (where it is sometimes mistaken for socialism), so that general practitioners and public health physicians can see themselves in alliance to shepherd the populace into healthy ways. Whilst this works for simple tasks, like cervical smear tests, it fails in complex ones, like reducing the rate of unwanted pregnancies or modifying multiple risk factors for heart disease; but nevertheless it offers an important sense of professional purpose and identity and has developed a momentum of its own that will become resource-hungry. Better this than the sale of packages of health promotion of dubious effectiveness but high profile, like screening 'check-ups', but perhaps better still the promotion of health can become part of the normal, everyday social agenda, as a form of personal participation in health maintainance that most citizens already strive to achieve, if only in limited ways. By loosing health promotion on the NHS the Conservatives may have introduced a competitor to the much vaunted principle of consumerism in health care - participation.

NEXT STEPS?

If we cannot return to the 'command and control' form of NHS that existed until 1991, and markets do not work satisfactorily in health care, what will? The straight answer is that we do not yet know, but a number of characteristics of a socially just and high quality health service suitable for a new century are discernible.

There is no escape from the funding issue. The Conservatives have attempted to transfer the responsibility for paying for health services to local commissioning agencies, aided by market mechanisms, and to a variable extent to the public, but this has exacerbated rather than eliminated the political problem of NHS funding. Although an incoming government will have no magic wand to wave that could create extra resources, the legacies of both long-term undercapitalisation and an inescapable gap between demand and supply will have to be faced. Methods like the Private Finance Initiative may be the Trojan Horse of privatisation when designed by the Conservatives, but, reconfigured to maximise public control, they could possibly help with the long-overdue renewal of NHS facilities, and the new government is likely to retain an interest in them. This will not help with the revenue problem, however, and extra public funding will be needed to restore some stability to the service as a whole, create some slack in the hospitals to avoid persistent bed shortages, develop primary care and meet the demands generated by demographic change and technological advance.

The NHS might need annual expenditure amounting to about 8 per cent of GNP (the EC average) for such renewal. From where could this money come? Direct taxation is the obvious answer, and there is some evidence that this would be acceptable to the majority of taxpayers, but a clear link to health services might be necessary, perhaps in the form of an earmarked tax. Reallocation of indirect taxation is another possibility, but implies that some other current beneficiary would lose revenue, unless VAT were increased to, say, 20 per cent. Creative solutions may be proffered: the National Lottery is a form of voluntary taxation that could fund the NHS, though it would be hard to see it as progressive; the pharmaceutical industry's expenditure on advertising and promotion of drugs would be a small but helpful contribution to NHS revenue. Whilst a new government may find the choices hard, and opt for a piecemeal approach through a number of mechanisms, the need to increase the proportion of GNP committed to health services is likely to force politicians towards either an earmarked tax or the German health insurance model, since these are essentially the same solution.[2] The political battle is likely to be around 'topping up' the benefits of the earmarked tax through private health insurance, with the right favouring a basic service so limited that all those who can insure themselves, whilst the left will favour a more comprehensive range of provision and tolerate private insurance as a preoccupation of the discontented affluent.

ORGANISATIONAL SLACK

This extra revenue is needed, in part at least, to purchase organisational slack for the NHS. The logic of the market requires providers to respond to rising demand by increasing supply, and to compete with each other by having enough spare capacity to meet variations in demand without being drained by too many underemployed staff and too much unused space. In the NHS the management of the market within a fixed central budget prevents variations in responsiveness by reducing spare capacity drastically. Instead of having too few hospital beds and too few operating theatre sessions, the NHS should have empty beds and staff working at less than optimal efficiency, at least some of the time. In the short term this appears uneconomic, but this judgement derives from an approach to economics as defined by accountants, rather than economists. The ward that runs at maximum capacity may lose beds assigned for elective surgery because of a sudden influx of trauma victims, and the planned surgery is postponed. The economic costs to the erstwhile patients, and through them to society, are not part of the accountant's equation, but they still count, and drive individuals and companies to the private sector, where time is understood as money. The opportunity costs of lack of organisational slack do not end there. The staff who have to work harder and harder to maintain throughput and reduce in-patient stays in their increasingly efficient ward may lose recuperation time between cases, have less control over their working pace and environment, and so become more prone to error, illness and 'burn out'. The consequences of the spread-sheet mentality for the NHS may be sickness absence, faster staff turnover, lowered morale, with less effort applied to tasks and difficulties in recruitment. Which professional group in the NHS is unfamiliar with these problems?

Another use for extra funding is in the expansion of community services and social care. There is less and less logic in the separation of health and social services, and their fusion now seems appropriate. This is easier to say than do, of course, because the two services have different cultures and a history of difficult relationships with each other. Social care is less glamorous and emotionally attractive than high technology medicine, and has usually lost out in the competition for resources. How will a new government overcome that historic legacy and shift the balance in favour of social care? Will *ad hoc* solutions be pursued, if only to create the impression of action whilst central problems and conflicts are avoided? Perhaps the solution lies in the creation of an open-ended budget for social care alongside the capitation-based budgets of the health service, to allow the rapid development of social services to levels commensurate with need. General practice had an open-ended budget for prescribing for most of the period from 1948 until now, and prescribing costs were kept relatively low (compared with Europe) through a centrally-negotiated price regulation process. General practitioners were also reimbursed on a carefully monitored but open-ended basis (the pool system), so that they could afford next year whatever they spent this year. The same approach might help haul social care out of its means-tested doldrums, without necessarily being enshrined as the only possible way of funding such services. A ten year phase of development, with open-ended budgets but carefully regulated spending, might be enough to repair the damage done to social care in the Thatcher period, and could then lead to a phase of slower, cash-limited development.

DIZZY WITH SUCCESS?

Ten years is a long time in the current timeframe of the NHS, where one year horizons seem normal and staff often last only two or three, but a slower cycle of change is now needed. The advantages of the purchaser-provider split may be enhanced by longer periods for discussion and negotiation about contracts, longer periods for service development and refinement, and more notice of changing purchasing intentions. The information needed to make decisions about allocation of resources are not necessarily available to planners, who must make 'best guess' estimates or stick with past practice, but extra time would allow that information to be gathered, change to be tested, and outcomes measured. Slowing the system down means abandoning the voluntarist mentality within the NHS management, and the ideology driving the NHS Executive down the market road. The assumption that the culture of the NHS can be transformed by forcing change on an unprepared and largely unwilling workforce, industrial structure and population has a bizarre parallel in the collectivisation of farming in the former USSR, where the immediate consequences were civil strife and food shortages, and the long-term consequence a fundamental and irreversible reduction in agricultural activity. The recent reformers have been partly dizzy with success and partly aware that they are failing to make their ideas take root, with the result that the balance in management is swinging away from market solutions that clearly do not work to management ones that appear no more helpful.[3]

Faced with resistance to change, zealous reformers redouble their pressure. In the NHS this takes the path of monetarising all relationships. Locally determined pay will solve the problem of recruitment of qualified staff, if only by poaching them from elsewhere, but at the expense of all staff in post wanting their posts similarly valued. If an anaesthetist post cannot be filled without offering £100,000 a year, the logic of the market (even in its managed form) says offer it. Existing anaesthetists then want parity, requiring cuts in other services to balance the budget. If waiting lists can be cleared by special payments to surgeons to do extra operations, all future requests for extra activity may be met with a request for extra payment. And if senior staff can opt to do or not do tasks that were once part of the function of their hospital or their department then their juniors can do the same, leaving their posts at 'clocking off time' even if work is incomplete or the next shift has not arrived. Abolition of the cash nexus needs to be a priority for the new government, and it can begin quickly by abandoning incentive systems that breed the monetarisation of relationships within hospital medicine, and by ending the fundholding experiment in general practice. The professional response is likely to be hostile to both moves, because doctors have had their long-standing preoccupation with money enhanced by Thatcherite ideology and because fundholding has enhanced the power as well as the income of a core group of general practitioners. A clash between the new government and the profession may come early in the process of undoing the damage of the reforms, around these issues, and is probably unavoidable. How could the government sensibly respond? Perhaps by leaving the fundholders' power largely undented, but within a more appropriate structure of locality commissioning that blends different perspectives and knowledge into the planning process, whilst making release of extra resources for hospital care (renewed organisational slack) contingent on professional co-operation, or at least acquiescence.

The demise of the fundholding experiment will be, in effect, the end of the dream of a 'primary care led NHS'. This has long been a slippery concept, and has outlived any usefulness it might have had. It was born when the right expropriated the ideas of (relatively) forward thinking general practitioners about the potential for enhanced medical care in the community, mostly through strengthened general practice, and converted it into a mechanism for shifting the NHS into the marketplace and introducing American-style 'Health Maintainance Organisations'. It always overvalued general practice as a contributor to medical care (as did the pioneer general practitioners themselves), and ignored the real trends within general practice to an industrial mode of activity with an increasingly semi-detached workforce that seemed a poor candidate for leadership of the NHS. The experience of fundholding could be drawn into locality planning of health services, where it would serve as a useful complement to public health and local government expertise, and the input of local community groups themselves.

COMMUNITY ORIENTATION

The perspective for the NHS that might then develop would be of community orientation of local services, driven by local need. The fusion of health and social care under local government responsibility, and the merger of professional and public perspectives in locality planning would allow two further changes to occur. Health promotion could become public property, as part of community development and of the agenda of schools, trades unions, churches and other voluntary organisations. And consumerism could be recast as participation, with balanced rights and responsibilities, not only at the community level but also in individual use of services. Here the slow cycles of change and the commitment to enhanced funding for health and social care, if necessary by increased but dedicated taxation, might act in synergy, allowing citizens rendered sceptical by a decade or more of sham consultations and economies with the truth to become actively involved in policymaking and to see the positive results of their efforts. The health service, in turn, will ask for their involvement in maintaining their own health and that of their fellow citizens, against all the health-damaging pressures of a commercialised society. The time it takes to discuss, understand and inform will itself act as a necessary brake on the cycle of change and limit the pressure for rapid solutions to problems that are at present forced on the NHS by excessively tight budget constraints and advocates of the market.

This approach could make the first decade of the next century a period of public involvement, just as the seventies were the years of management, the eighties was the decade of health economics, and the nineties of managed markets. Each new phase has been an attempt to overcome the problems of the previous period, and each has produced its new problems. Public participation will be no exception, and its limitations and risks are already evident. How will knowledge of the effectiveness of treatments balance the emotional pull of shroud-waving? Will public responsibility for health promotion grow too fast, stigmatising the smoker as much as the drug user, the over-eater as much as the heavy drinker, and produce a kind of 'health fascism' that will generate resistance to change and to health itself? And can the different interests and views of citizens and NHS professionals and managers ever be satisfactorily synthesised in a society that is becoming increasingly pluralistic?

There do not appear ready made answers to these questions, and most of them will have to be worked through to find practical solutions. Although an Aneurin Bevan-like individual might emerge at some point to resolve the conflict of ideas and draw together an alliance of disparate interest groups in favour of bold change, no such character is yet in sight. Nor are the circumstances propitious for such a Big Idea to emerge. The 'crisis' of the NHS has not evolved sufficiently from its origins in the market reforms of 1991 to warrant anything more than relatively minor policy adjustments, and public opinion has yet to deliver an overwhelmingly negative verdict on the Thatcher and Major administrations. Only social care could be seen as ripe for the kind of qualitative change in thinking and organisation that gave birth to the NHS, because it has never had a growth phase and the experience of professional development comparable to that of medicine. The political turbulence around health care seems likely to continue for the foreseeable future, but the problems of social care may promote major political change earlier.

HISTORIC COMPROMISE

What compromises might have to be made in the NHS, in the next few years? Fundholding, performance related pay, and local pay bargaining are poor contenders for political survival because of their costly destabilising effects. The

Private Finance Initiative is a major risk factor for privatisation, but might survive in truncated form as a short-term solution to the problem of under-capitalisation. The 'primary care leadership' for the NHS will be rebadged to reflect its disparate membership and community orientation, and Evidence Based Medicine will fade into the background as its apparently magical properties to solve problems themselves melt into air. The purchaser-provider split is likely to remain as a useful mechanism for stabilising and managing the service, although it will need to be relabelled in an acceptable way that reflects the drive to slow change, demonetarisation of relationships and increasing public involvement.

Perhaps most important among the surviving themes of the Conservative reforms will be the public-private mix of services. The boundaries of public and private care will be difficult to define clearly, and the more civil society plays a part in the shaping of local service development, the more blurred these boundaries will become. Organisations outside the national and local state are already playing roles in the provision of health and social care, and some of these (like pharmacy, dentistry, optician services and many nursing and residential homes for older people) are openly commercial in their operation. The political divide could run along the line between commercial operation 'for profit' and non-profit activity, the former being the solution proffered by the Right and the latter the favoured solution of the left, but this does not clarify the situation and may not assist in developing policy. General practice could be seen as a 'for profit' enterprise whilst private health insurance companies can operate 'non-profit' hospitals, and the new government is unlikely to rule against the former and in favour of the latter.

The conflict between public and private may be resolved by focusing attention on control of services, and rewriting the NHS Act accordingly. If the health services committee of a local government chooses to contract with private services to meet its obligations to its community, and to fulfil the tasks required of it by the NHS Executive, then it is acting in the interests of the public. If it chooses to favour private sector services without fulfilling its obligations to its community and the overarching national objectives it will be acting in a partisan fashion and be subject to disciplinary action from the NHS Executive. And any successor government that insists that any or all activity must be offered to the private sector will be stepping outside the NHS Act and acting unlawfully. By making the contracting process open, within an explicit framework of expectations and obligations, to local communities and the overall health of the nation, political regulation of the NHS can be used to resist its commercial subversion.

Many of those who denounced the Conservative reforms from a trades union rostrum or on a march down Whitehall will not feel comfortable with an historic compromise with the right, but the truth is that it has always been thus, and there are no signs that that the mould of NHS development can be broken. Idealisation of the NHS before Thatcher does not impress most of those who grew up with it, especially if it was their employer, and does little to orientate us towards the society of the 21st century. The old NHS was a piece of 'actually existing socialism' that could not adapt to change fast enough to continue unscathed but that was valuable enough to survive. Its strengths have been sufficient to prevent its wholesale privatisation, leaving us with the problem of how to revive and renew a comprehensive health service, largely free at the time of need and funded from taxation, when the social and political conditions that made such a service essential have long gone.

Notes

1. *Konflictpartnerschaft* has replaced *Sozialpartnerschaft* as a description of relationships between unions and employers in the Germany economy, partly because it is a more accurate description of the real situation but also because German employers need to take a more aggressive stance against a formidable union movement, in order to lever higher productivity. The situation is analogous in the NHS, where managerial power needs to be enhanced to balance that of the professions, especially Medicine.

2. German health insurance is not insurance in the usual sense, since citizens do not pay a premium related to their risk, but a fixed proportion of their income, so that those with high incomes subsidise those with lower incomes. Those without income have benefits that are paid for by those who are earning, introducing a further element of solidarity to the funding system.

3. When the *British Medical Journal* focused on Stalinism in the NHS its authors interpreted it as the climate of secrecy that develops in market relationships, rather than as the heroic, overspeedy change that the USSR experienced in its Stalinist phase. Perhaps this medical misperception is not surprising, given the medical profession's own tendencies to heroism and the belief that everything is possible.

NOTES ON CONTRIBUTORS

Steve Harrison has taught and researched at the University of Leeds since 1978, where he is currently Reader in Health Policy and Politics at the Nuffield Institute for Health. His interests are in both the macro-politics of the NHS, especially its policies, organisation and governance, and its micro-politics, including the relationships between managers and non-professional workers. His most recent book is *Controlling Health Professionals* (with Christopher Pollitt).

David Hunter has been Director of the Nuffield Institute for Health at Leeds University since 1989. In 1991 he became Professor of Health Policy and Management at the university. He has published widely on aspects of health and social care policy and management practice, including the issue of rationing in health care and the problem of accountability in the NHS. He contributes a monthly column to the *Health Service Journal*.

Steve Iliffe is a general practioner in north-west London, Reader in Primary Care at University College London Medical School and a member of the editorial board of *Health Matters*.

Alison McCallum is Senior Lecturer in the Department of Primary Care and Population Sciences at the Royal Free Hospital School of Medicine in London and a practising public health doctor in north-east London. Her interests include education in public health and health promotion, development and evaluation of effective public health interventions. She is a memeber of the British Regional Heart Study Research Team.

James Munro is Clinical Lecturer in Epidemiology at the University of Sheffield. He worked as a hospital doctor in the NHS before specialising in public health medicine, and has been a member of the editorial group of *Health Matters* magazine since 1986. His research interests include exercise in the elderly, equity in access to health care, and changing clinical behaviour.

Allyson Pollock is Senior Lecturer in Public Health Medicine at St George's Hospital Medical School in London, and consultant in Public Health Medicine at Merton, Sutton and Wandsworth health authority. Her major areas of work and publication have been in cancer epidemiology, long term care and health policy, including rationing and the reform of health and social care. She is currently on a Harkness Fellowship in the USA studying managed care, long term care and the private sector.

Geof Rayner works as a consultant to public and voluntary sector organisations, having worked previously in local government and universities. He is a trustee of the national Council of Voluntary Organisations, an associate member of a London health authority and secretary of the Public Health Alliance, and has written widely on health and social services policy.

Alan Walker is Professor of Social Policy at the University of Sheffield. He has been researching and writing on the subjects of community care and older people for more than 20 years. He is responsible for some of the leading works on the nature and meaning of community care. His most recent book is *Changing services for older people* (with Lorna Warren).

Index